Alec
"You Talk
Whip One M ... **Up**
The Flagpole The Next.

"Just when I think you're showing an interest, you get me all twisted around like last year's baling wire."

"Am I asking stupid questions?"

"It's just hard to figure out a woman who, in the middle of an explanation of cattle rustling, asks a question that reminds a man he got caught buck naked in front of her."

"Since I bared my soul at the creek, I guess I still feel the need to keep you a little off balance."

"There's a look in your eye that's pure challenge. Makes a foreman forget his place."

Dory laughed. "I'm sorry you don't like my look. If I've done something—"

"Baroness, that look could melt a man into his boots."

Dear Reader:

Welcome to Silhouette Desire – provocative, compelling, contemporary love stories written by and for today's woman. These are stories to treasure.

Each and every Silhouette Desire is a wonderful romance in which the emotional and the sensual go hand in hand. When you open a Desire, you enter a whole new world – a world that has, naturally, a perfect hero just waiting to whisk you away! A Silhouette Desire can be light-hearted or serious, but it will always be satisfying.

We hope you enjoy this Silhouette today – and will go on to enjoy many more.

Please write to us:

Jane Nicholls
Silhouette Books
PO Box 236
Thornton Road
Croydon
Surrey
CR9 3RU

LESLIE
DAVIS GUCCIONE
ROUGH AND READY

Silhouette Desire

Originally Published by Silhouette Books
a division of
Harlequin Enterprises Ltd.

*First published in Great Britain in 1992
by Silhouette Books, Eton House, 18-24 Paradise Road,
Richmond, Surrey TW9 1SR*

© Leslie Davis Guccione 1992

*Silhouette, Silhouette Desire and Colophon are
Trade Marks of Harlequin Enterprises B.V.*

ISBN 0 373 58657 4

22-9210

Made and printed in Great Britain

LESLIE DAVIS GUCCIONE

lives with her husband and three children in a state of semichaos in an historic sea captains' district south of Boston. When she's not at her typewriter, she's actively researching everything from sailboats to cranberry bogs. What free time she has is spent sailing and restoring her circa-1827 Cape Cod cottage. Her ideas for her books are based on the world around her—as she states, "Romance is right under your nose." She has also written under the name Leslie Davis.

Other Silhouette Books by Leslie Davis Guccione

Silhouette Desire

Before the Wind
*Bittersweet Harvest
*Still Waters
*Something in Common
*Branigan's Touch
*Private Practice
A Gallant Gentleman

Branigan Brothers series

For Ted and Dorrie, the real Buck and Baroness

One

"**I**'m back, did you miss me?"

Dory Lydon tossed a stone at the deserted gully ledge and listened to the Montana wind carry her voice. With her face to the heavens, she gazed from one vista to another. How could she have forgotten how beautiful it was?

She continued gingerly along the rocky creek bed to the area where it dipped through a crevice and tumbled over mineral-rich boulders. The vastness of the rolling hills, the endless Montana sky, and the grazing Hereford cattle of the thirty-thousand acre Rocker L Ranch had left her breathless. She stood still and let the overpowering sense of space engulf her, savoring the pounding of her heart. From this beloved spot, it would have been easy to imagine that nothing had changed in the years since her childhood visits.

As a last minute substitute for her brother, Dory was still dressed for the long trip out from Philadelphia. The plane change in Minneapolis, the delay in Billings, not to mention the time zone difference, had left her exhausted. This was what she needed to revive herself, the hike out, the stream and a headful of memories.

She marveled at the scenery as she searched for the secluded swimming spot she'd loved as a kid. For late June, it was deeper than she'd remembered, swollen by a thankfully wet spring. All the shadowy hiding places were still there. A long-ago crop of Rocker L cowboys had told her they were filled with the bones of Montana bandits caught in six-gun crossfire or the bitter winter weather. Dory smiled to ease the lump in her throat. The spot was every bit as enticing on this dusty summer afternoon as it had been the first time she'd splashed in it as a six-year-old.

All the way out from the ranch on her solitary walk, through the hillocks of ponderosa, to the meandering rock-and-crevice branch of the Musselshell River, Dory had tried to concentrate on her mother's determination to keep the Rocker L financially sound and her own cockeyed insistence that she was capable of standing in for John C. Lydon III—her brother Jace. He was the Lydon that Heartland Mining Company was expecting in the office Monday morning.

Ranch manager Red O'Brien had met her plane, and deposited her at the guest cottage. It wasn't until he'd set down her luggage that she had discovered the cottage currently housed the foreman, Alec McDowell, one of the five employees who were no more than names on a financial sheet. "Of course we would have bunked your brother right in with Alec," Red had quipped.

"I'm sorry if I'm disrupting things."

"You're a Lydon, same as the rest. It's about time you took an interest in what's yours. Besides, Alec's camped out on the North Range and likely to be there right through your stay. If he returns before Monday, I'll put him up in the main house." Red had then gone off to meet the cowhands mending fences. Dory had all the privacy she needed.

When she reached the beloved watering spot she stopped and inhaled, then forced herself to concentrate on the scenery. The unrelenting ache in her was not from the unstable economics of ranching, or the major decisions that lay ahead. Dory Lydon had been emotionally unstrung by a man—again—and the resulting misery smothered her good intentions like range dust kicked up by a stampeding herd.

However, not one inch of the landscape held any association with her ex-fiancé. She scooped up a handful of water with a silent salute to her brainstorm. "I was right, this is the cure. Tyler Baldridge, out of sight, out of mind."

She was half inclined to strip down and take a dip, as if she could cleanse herself of the misery Tyler had inflicted on her. Skinny-dipping, however, was not on her agenda, neither was wallowing in self-pity. It was time to look fractured romance in the eye and get on with her business obligations.

As she sat on a particularly uncomfortable rock and stuck her bare feet into the tumbling water, loose stones scuttled behind her. She spun around as her spine tingled. "Hello?"

The wind moaned.

Dory listened, then turned back and rolled up the cuffs of her linen slacks. She watched the water tumble over her toes. Her nerves still danced as she looked across at the empty ledge. Not so much as a shadow moved. She rolled her pants to her knees, then waded in.

Her sixth sense refused to be silenced. Something kept her heart hammering and she fought the urge to back up and return to the compound. Instead she spun around as she conjured up a coiled predator. It wouldn't be the first time she'd spotted a snake sunning itself. The ledge was still empty.

"Is somebody there?" She listened for a hiss.

The Montana wind whistled in the scrub pine.

"Hello?" She pressed her hand on her heart, wishing, as in the old days, that her brother Jace were with her.

"No snakes and no humans," she told herself as she turned back to the water. She waded deeper and wiggled her polished toenails as she pondered.

"Speaking of snakes," she said to the air. "Speaking of a no good, no future, two-legged, self-centered snake..." She cleared her throat. "It's over." She said it out loud, twice, as if the sound of her voice might deepen her conviction. Dory's heart ached, but the sardonic comment was laced with sarcasm. She kicked at a pool of water.

"It's over, Tyler." The sun began to burn as she untied the designer scarf of hot pink rosebuds from around her throat. With a twist, she tucked her mane of chestnut-colored hair up into an impromptu hairband, then grabbed a handful of stones and began to pace. She tossed them gently at first, then with the determination of a Little League pitcher.

Plunk. "It's over. I've tried everything I know to make it work." *Plunk.* "I had every right to bring expectations to this relationship, expectations as important as yours." *Plunk.* "One of those expectations was faithfulness." She threw a stone into a pool. "Commitment." She turned and tossed another at the crevice where she'd imagined the rattler to be basking. "Commitment has to be the unshakable base when two people—" she cleared the tremble in her voice "—when two people . . ."

She hucked the last stone hard into the shadowed recess where it disappeared with a thud. "Snake." The ache inside her was working its way up into the back of her throat. That old, familiar burn made her clench her teeth. She pressed her hands against the unwelcome tears she knew were next.

"Not here," she said as her voice cracked. "Damn you, Tyler."

She stumbled into midstream, up to her shins, and sat on an exposed rock. "I want you out of my life, Tyler Baldridge. Out!" As her tears spilled, she cupped the water and splashed her face. An unexpected sob broke from her throat in a gasp and she splashed furiously, soaking her blouse, her bra, and a good portion of her hair that had fallen out from under the scarf. "When will I learn?" she hiccuped.

Tyler wasn't worth her grief and she fought it furiously, valiantly, until there wasn't enough fight left. Her hollow heart filled then overflowed with tears she'd stored during weeks and weeks of misery. Alone, already soaked, she gave in and let her tears run.

"The devil can have all of them, every last male east of the Mississippi," was about all she could manage.

She cried long and hard, damning Tyler, damning herself, damning love until the relief she knew was in her somewhere began to fill the void. She grumbled and sniffed until composure returned. As she hiccuped, her breasts heaved against her clammy, clinging blouse and she pulled the fabric away from her bra. Dory kicked the water as she stepped back to shore.

She dug her heel into the mud. "You'd think I'd know by now. You'd think I'd learn. A Christmas wedding . . ." She shuddered again.

As she scrambled to the shore, another cascading rock bounced off the ledge in front of her. Again, she snapped to attention as the hairs rose along the back of her neck. She wiped, then shielded her eyes and squinted into the blue-black shadows. "Who's there?"

The stream gurgled behind her. She sniffed away the last of her tears. "Selfish, two-timing, egotistical snake." She tossed a final stone into the cave-dark hollow. This time a faint guttural noise, decidedly animal, perhaps human, stopped her heart. "Hello?" She was greeted with the unmistakable sound of stone over gravel.

Her East Coast imagination kicked in again. She grabbed a rock and raised it in self-defence imagining a wounded mountain lion chewing on the remains of a Rocker L calf. The only reply was the thundering in her chest, and the sweet chill of her gooseflesh. She stepped closer and squinted while her eyes adjusted to the dark.

"Stay where you are," boomed out at her so unexpectedly that she cried out. The deep, masculine command was followed by the blur of a dim silhouette of a head and shoulders.

Dory froze and held her breath against the conjured image of a crazed lunatic and the barrel of a rifle. It was time to beat a hasty retreat. She took a giant step backward.

"Stop."

The command shocked her into obeying.

"Turn around," the voice added.

Turn around? It was terrifying enough facing the shadowy figure. Instead Dory drew herself up to her full five feet ten inches, gripped the stone, raised her hand, and aimed again for the shadows.

The voice rumbled. "That's enough rock tossing. You've hit me once already. Drop the rock. I'm not out to hurt you."

"You can't get away with this," she replied, with her hand still poised. A horse whinnied somewhere beyond her vision.

There was a guttural snort. "For the love of Pete, *getting away* is all I'm trying to do."

Alarm continued to sound in Dory's head. Thirty thousand rolling Montana acres, an hour's walk back to the cowboy-less compound and she was face-to-shadow with a heaven-knows-what-he'd-done fugitive.

Before she could decide what to do, a hand flashed into the daylight. She screamed and glimpsed a blur of bare arm, then chest as she was grabbed. The figure spun her around to face the stream. The vicelike grip held as her arm was yanked to her side.

From behind, the voice muttered, "Good God, woman, quiet down! You'll wake the dead. Hush and stay as you are." The rock was pried from her fingers. "On second thought, hand me your scarf."

Terrified as she was, Dory still managed to arch her back and pull herself up to her full height. "No."

A hand pulled the scarf from her hair. She fully expected to feel the bite of the silk at her throat, her wrists, or at the very least, around her eyes.

"Look," she tried, "I don't know what you want—"

"I want out of here."

She swallowed her terror until a hand on her shoulder made her jump again. She was nudged forward.

"Who are you and what—"

"Stop fighting me every step of the way!"

"What do you expect me to do!"

"For the past twenty minutes you've been standing in this crick, giving me an earful, mooning over your terminal heartache, damning some guy named Baldridge like he left you at the altar."

Beneath the tumble of hair, Dory's ears burned and her shoulder blades itched where she imagined her assailant to be staring. "How dare you . . ."

"How dare *me!* Next thing I know you're taking out that fury by using me for target practice."

"I had no idea . . ."

"I'm no eavesdropper. All I want is to get out of here. Trouble is, I get no indication you're likely to quit any time soon and you've got me trapped."

Determined to get the upper hand, she raised her chin. "There are half a dozen ways out of here. You're certainly not trapped."

"Trapped, woman, like a cow in a branding pen. You're chucking rocks, crying and caterwauling all between me and my clothes."

"Clothes?"

"Lady, I'm buck naked."

Two

Dory was too full of fear, adrenaline, humiliation and self-righteous indignation to do more than sputter. "What do you want? You had no right to hide in there. Who do you think you are, spying and eavesdropping?"

She spun around to face her tormentor and the remaining tirade stuck in her throat. She was face-to-face with six feet, two inches of green-eyed anger in the form of one decidedly broad-shouldered, narrow-hipped, naked-except-for-her-scarf stranger. "Good Lord, you are naked!" Dory swiped at her tear-stained cheeks and flushed scarlet.

Masculine appraisal came in one slow, scathing glance. "You thought I was lying?" The stranger's unswerving glare belied any shred of embarrassment, despite his own flush from throat to scalp.

Dory tried to match his glance. His thick hair was disheveled and damp. His face was layered with remnants of range dust, broken by clean streaks left by water or sweat. There was a tan line across one arm, another at his throat and an angry cut on his shoulder. She looked down to his left hand—wide open and discreetly pressed with her patch of pink rosebuds against his groin. She chuckled and just as quickly glanced up to his face.

His jaw was covered with a healthy growth of beard and a hint of crow's feet accentuated a clear angry gaze that was pure frustration. He motioned with his chin. "Turn back around and don't move. All I want in this world is to get my clothes."

"I'm not turning my back on you, naked or not. Where are they? I'll get them."

"The hell you will." His expression changed from angry to incredulous, then back to angry. "Mood you're in, there's no telling what you'd do with them. I don't know who you are, or what you're up to, but this mess needs straightening out." He stabbed at a rock. "Sit down there and don't move. I'll be right back."

How naive did he think she was? She shoved her feet into her shoes. The moment she could hear that he'd started off, she bolted. Dory lit out in the opposite direction, along the creek bed and up the ridge toward what she prayed had not been more than her imagination.

"Hey!" reverberated below her.

As she rounded the boulder, an untethered horse raised its head.

"Thank God," she cried. Without so much as a glance backward, she mounted the dusty gelding, dug her heels into its flank, and took off for the compound.

Dory came in sight of the empty stables tight-lipped, damp-eyed and flaming with humiliation. She left the horse in the corral, as she'd always done as a visiting teenager, and scrambled toward the shelter of the guest cottage where she was staying, half praying that by some quirk, Red might have returned. The compound was deserted.

She fought tears as she climbed the steps of the neat two-story cottage, built to accommodate the far-flung Lydons who returned for vacations and periodic business meetings. She sank down on the porch bench as common sense returned. The cowboy's deep tenor voice had been distraught, not threatening. The tone in his commands had been frustration, not menace.

Had she been thinking straight, had she been clear-headed or calm, or even in control of the situation at the creek, she might have realized what was evident to her now.

She glanced across the yard to the bunkhouse and groaned. The grizzled stranger was very likely one of "hers," one of the hands taking a break from fence-mending. After half a dozen deep breaths, she let herself into the cottage, desperate for a shower and a clear head.

Letting herself inside didn't help. She entered, suitcase in hand, only to be enveloped, not by the nostalgic musty smell of a cottage opened only for Lydon visits, but by the overwhelming feeling that she was intruding on her foreman's privacy.

"What a dismal start," she muttered. She felt like a trespasser, at the stream and in what was now someone else's home.

The cottage wasn't as she'd remembered. The living room was furnished comfortably. One wall was bookcases, the others displayed handsome Crow and Cheyenne blankets and artifacts. She glanced at a photograph of a man who looked to be in his late forties. He and a teenager sat astride quarter horses in chaps and spurs, Stetsons low on their foreheads, masking their features.

She picked up the frame and touched the face of the man she assumed to be her foreman. Alec McDowell was a person, perhaps a single father supporting the child in the photo, a man dependent on the economy of the Rocker L, dependent on the decisions of the Lydons, dependent on what lay ahead during this visit.

Dory put the photo back. As tempting as it would have been to peruse the shelves, she hurried past the couch to the door leading to the bedrooms. She chose the second one, with twin beds, which had always been hers. Now it was as overtly masculine as the rest of the rooms. There was no feeling that she'd ever been there. From the dishes on the kitchen drainboard to the photograph in the living room, the cottage contained someone else's personality.

She snapped on the bedroom radio already tuned to a blaring country and western station, loud enough to be heard in the adjoining bathroom. As she showered, reason returned completely, which only deepened her humiliation. No doubt the cowboy was as embarrassed as she. With any luck at all he'd steer clear of her for the duration of her visit. She hoped he had the maturity to keep the episode to himself and not make her the butt of bunkhouse humor. In deference to who she was, she assumed he wouldn't dare.

Dory raised her face to the spray and sighed as the water sluiced over her. Neither Jace nor her mother would have ever gotten off to such a ridiculous start. She thought about her scarf and smiled. The hapless ranch hand's desperation made her chuckle and before she knew it, she was laughing as hard as she'd been crying.

Obligation, Lydon, she told herself as she shampooed her hair. Embarrassed or not, she had an obligation to check on the injured cowboy. The last thing she needed was a stubborn ranch hand refusing medical treatment out of spite or embarrassment.

Dory rinsed and winced at the thought of confessing her behavior to Red O'Brien. She cringed at the inevitable ribbing her family and Red would heap on her, once the story got out.

When she'd toweled off, she plaited her wet hair into a French braid that accentuated her aristocratic features, then pulled on the requisite jeans and chambray shirt. With confession on her mind, she came back into the living room. Her heart jumped into her throat.

The cowboy, in all his disheveled glory, was leaning back in the easy chair next to the fireplace. His eyes were closed and his head was cocked to one side. He was holding an ice-filled dish towel pressed against his right shoulder.

His long legs were now jeans-clad and stretched out in front of him, resting, bootless, on the ottoman. There was a hole in the toe of his sock and his tired burgundy flannel shirt was unbuttoned, revealing his muscular chest. His hair was damp and, without the dirt, thick and wheat-colored.

At the sound of her footsteps, he said "Jace Lydon," with his eyes closed. "If you still don't take the longest showers in the county. I thought I'd miss you completely this trip, but the damnedest thing's just happened. Some woman, I suppose a friend of Ginny O'Brien's—"

Dory cleared her throat. "I'm not Jace."

The cowboy opened his eyes, swore a blue streak, and sat bolt upright. "You!"

Dory's shredded emotions stirred. Guilt burned behind her breastbone. "I'm here in his place."

"Where?"

"The Rocker L."

"And my house?"

"I'm sure you know this is the Lydon guest cottage. Red put me here."

"It was you in the shower?" He glared.

"Yes."

"Sorry I didn't know. I could have barged in and evened the score." Although he looked as if he might have regretted the outburst, he simply thrust his dish towel in the air. "Ice. For the swelling."

Dory stayed where she was, disconcerted by her physical response to him. "Once I reached home—"

"Home?"

"Once I got back here, to the compound, it occurred to me that you might be one of our employees."

He was still all edges and angles, but fatigue had deepened his squint as he looked up at her. His wide open wariness struck a chord. "Meaning I might be a ranch hand as opposed to a naked, murdering, rapist burglar."

She flushed. "Well, yes."

"Or a professional gun-toting eavesdropper."

"You seem to have made yourself at home. I assume that means you're the foreman."

"Right on the money."

"There was no pack on your saddle. I thought the foreman would probably have a pack for camping out."

"You're speaking of the saddle of the horse you stole."

"I—"

"Leaving a man without his horse is a hanging offense."

"You terrified me. Nevertheless, I was about to ride back and look for you."

"Leaving a lathered, half beat, saddled horse uncurried in a corral would get you fired, terrified or not. When you found me, I was just taking some time to wash off the dust. The stream's about a half hour ride from the ridge of the north range."

"I'm sorry."

"When—exactly—did you come to your senses?"

"When I got back here. I suppose I deserve your sarcasm, but I was out in the middle of nowhere."

"So was I."

"I was in strange territory. You scared me so badly, I didn't stop to think until I was home. Here." To fight her humiliation Dory concentrated on the blood on his shoulder. "You're still bleeding," she added as she reached for the towel.

He grabbed her again by the wrist. "That's close enough."

"Ow."

"Self-preservation instinct."

"Did I do that?"

"It sure wasn't the crick tossing rocks at me."

"Maybe you should see a doctor."

He let go of her. "Look, it's done. I came back to the ranch to take care of it."

Guilt wound itself through all of Dory's other emotions. "I'm sorry, honestly. If you'd called out when I first arrived, this wouldn't have happened. You should have said something to let me know you were there. I sensed it. That's why you scared me so badly."

"Scared *you?* I've been out on the range looking for people like you." He gave her another head-to-toe appraisal. "Not exactly like you. I tried to figure out who the heck you were as I *walked* back here."

"Jace had business commitments, so I flew out in his place. I'm Doris Lydon, Jace's sister. I suppose it's a bit late for introductions."

He groaned. "Doris Lydon, cattle baroness. I've had all the introduction I need."

"I'm sorry. I wish I could make the whole episode disappear."

The cowboy put the towel back on his shoulder and winced. "Might help if *you* disappeared."

"I'll be gone Monday afternoon."

"Three days between now and then. You've checked on me. I'm fine. Now leave me what's left of my dignity."

"*Your* dignity!"

He raised his eyebrows. "Lost yours, too, there for a while."

It wasn't enough that the cowboy was drop-dead handsome, unabashed about his nudity, and nursing a wound she'd inflicted. All that she could live down.

What made Dory's face hot and her stomach knot was the thought of her own behavior. She looked down at the man stretched out in front of her. "You sat on that ledge and witnessed the complete unraveling of my dignity. I've been exposed as much as you. More so. I feel like a teenager whose diary's been read to an audience."

"Kind of evens us up."

"I'd like to forget the entire episode."

"I'm game."

Dory concentrated again on his shoulder. "Good. I'm responsible for this and I'd like to make sure you give the wound proper attention. I know as the foreman you're in charge of the cowhands. I was planning to report it to Red. I'll explain everything to him and take full responsibility."

"You planning to spell it all out?"

"All Red needs to know is that I was in the stream, threw some rocks and hit you by accident."

"That version would save your dignity."

"That version would save *yours*."

For the first time, the cowboy grinned. "The cattle baroness thought I was a marauding outlaw. Green as the spring pasture," he added under his breath, then sat up.

Dory looked at the photo on the mantle. "I thought you were older."

"Since you didn't recognize me with my clothes off, can't say I'm surprised you didn't recognize me with my clothes on, either."

Three

"Alec McDowell in the flesh." Dory chuckled at her joke. "Why didn't you tell me who you were out there?"

"Introduce myself?" He looked incredulous. "Plum slipped my mind, being buck naked and all, with nothing between us but your scarf. To tell you the truth, I gave half a thought to heading straight back to my campsite."

"I was every bit as embarrassed as you."

"Embarrassment, hell. I meant for safety's sake."

She flushed again. "You seem determined to make me feel ridiculous."

"About as ridiculous as I looked on that ledge."

How he'd looked had nothing to do with ridiculous. She'd chew cottonwood bark, however, before she'd admit that internally she was still reacting to her glimpse of his hard, lean body. She looked through the window at the bunkhouse and deliberately changed the subject. "If you're not going back out to the camp-site, Red will put you up in the main house while I'm here."

"Plenty of room where we are."

"I hardly think that's appropriate."

"It was a joke. When my headache stops scream-ing and my shoulder loosens up I will head back out. For now the bunkhouse suits me."

"But in your position—"

"Which position would that be?"

"You're the foreman, in charge of the hands."

"Scratch the surface, we're all cowboys under-neath."

"And not ones for being told where to sleep."

"Not ones for being told much of anything. Keep your distance," he added as she bent forward.

Dory leaned over him. "Like it or not, this is my responsibility. I simply want to make sure you're all right."

"That's far enough."

"Please, just let me take a look at your shoulder. I can see the wound a lot easier than you."

"Stop calling it a *wound!* You make it sound like I got shot up in a barroom or just returned from the front lines."

"Cut, then. Please, it needs attention."

"It's getting attention, my attention. I don't want your doctoring."

She might have taken him at his word, but since she was no longer avoiding looking at him, it was easy to see the pain in his expression. His green eyes were dark and his handsome features were drawn.

"How old are you?"

"Thirty-one. Why?"

"I thought the photograph on the mantle was of you and your son."

"Been snooping?"

"Certainly not. It's right there, in plain sight."

With a grimace, the foreman turned to look at it. "It is me, me and my father. I was fourteen."

Thirty-one. He looked younger, almost vulnerable. "Is your father a rancher?"

"He was a manager, died the year that picture was taken."

"I'm sorry."

Alec shrugged. "I've done all right. Don't come any closer."

Dory looked through the window to the bunkhouse. "Any cowboys in there?"

"Soon."

"But nobody's around yet—to tease you about accepting some doctoring from the boss."

"Referring to yourself?"

"I was trying to lighten the atmosphere, but yes, I guess I was."

With discretion this time, he again sized her up. "Hell, woman, I command too much respect for any of them to dare."

"That's why we hired you." She smiled and gently pushed his hand and the toweling to one side. When he didn't object, she did her best to relax.

"Don't get too close, the aroma of horse and cow hanging on me'll melt the nose of a greenhorn."

"I'm no stranger to stables."

"No man's a pretty sight, coming in after four days out."

"I thought the branding was all done."

"Rustlers."

Dory took the towel from him. "Goodness."

"You look skeptical." He scooted back into the cushions.

"It's tough to tell when you're pulling my leg."

"Cattle rustling's no joke. The bulk of your herd, except for the breeders and cows, is out to pasture in the north range. Boots Jensen came across an opening in the fence, just the other side of a sheltered gully. Tough to spot, even from horseback. I've been out looking for tracks."

"From the rustlers' horses?"

"Trucks."

"Stupid question, I guess."

"For an eastern greenhorn, no. For the owner of a thirty-thousand acre cattle ranch, yes. You come all this way to decide which one you might be? Or to wash away traces of that 'snake' Baldridge?"

"We were talking about rustling."

"So we were. I've been tracking tire marks."

"Then you found evidence?"

"Evidence? Yes. Mostly, I've been out there lying in wait."

"Where do you sleep?"

"With that kind of work, you don't, much. I took a bedroll and spent most of the time in a stand of ponderosa that runs above the pasture. More than likely you've lost a few head of cattle. Thieves'll come in at night, run a collie out to pasture, herd what they can transport right into the back of a truck. A few aren't missed. Simple as opening a can of beans for some."

"I didn't know."

"That's obvious."

"You don't mince words."

"Considering the condition I'm in, you're lucky I can put a sentence together. Might do you some good if you did take an interest in your ranch. Concentrate on something besides your misery."

His blunt reply stung. "Despite what you saw and heard, I'm not miserable. I run a business of my own at home. The ranch has always been the responsibility of my mother and brother—and all of you, for that matter. That's what we pay Red and the rest of you for. Did you catch the thieves?"

He studied her. "Not yet."

"You don't have much use for me, do you?"

In reply, he pulled away. "You cut right to the bone, don't you?"

"You don't seem to be one for small talk."

He turned his appraising glance to the room. "Red O'Brien's a fair man to work for. Maggie Lydon's tough, but she's got a good reputation, too. I'm proud to work for both of them."

"That's not what I asked."

"I don't have much use for your antics or your doctoring, that's all."

Dory considered his diplomacy. There was no purpose in belaboring the point, and no denying she was a neophyte on her own territory. She turned her attention back to his face. "Stop trying to burrow into the chair. Why are men always so stubborn?"

"Out here it depends entirely on who we brush up against. There's a certain kind of woman just brings out the worst in a man. Can't speak for those east of the Mississippi."

"'East of the Mississippi.' What did you do, memorize everything I said in that stream?"

"Wasn't much else to listen to and I was in no position to leave."

This time it was Dory who flushed.

Alec smiled at her embarrassment. "Lord only knows what you did to Tyler to make him so ornery."

"Tyler Baldridge is none of your business. You've made it clear that you think I'm a naive meddler, but I don't need your opinions on my private life, Alec. May I call you Alec?"

"You had something else in mind?"

She paused, anxious to have the upper hand. "Now that you mention it, *Alec McDowell*'s not much of a cowboy name. 'Buck' suits you."

"Buck."

"As in Buck Naked. It has a certain cowboy air."

Alec's eyes widened in surprise and then he laughed. It did his face a world of good. "Buck. I suppose we both got our fill of humiliation this afternoon. What am I supposed to call you?"

"Stick to Baroness. It has a nice ring. I'm sure it suits your opinion of me."

"That it does." He tilted his head in frank appraisal that dampened her palms.

She moved her hand and he flinched. "Does it hurt that much? I haven't even touched you." She smiled. "Cowboys are supposed to be stoic, sun-leathery skin, tough as an elephant's hide, with an ego to boot."

He cocked one eyebrow. "Get your expertise from Western novels or a movie theater back east of the Mississippi?"

"I've spent plenty of time out here."

"Not recently. You about finished looking me over?"

She tried to look disgusted. "I don't think it needs stitches."

"Of course it doesn't. Get along. Aren't you due at Red's for dinner or something?"

"Yes, but there's plenty of time. Stay right there." She straightened up. "There's hydrogen peroxide in my bathroom."

"Damn it, woman—"

"I'll be right back. Sit still so you don't get blood on that chair of yours."

"I don't need—"

"Yes you do. It's just simple first aid."

"*Your* doctoring's what I don't need. I've been tending scrapes just fine, thank you."

"Can't stand advice from a woman?"

"I work for your mother, don't I?"

"Only in theory. Red runs the operation."

He shrugged. "A woman gives me advice needs following, I'll take it, same as a man's."

Dory stood up and looked at him. She snapped her fingers. "You're afraid it'll sting. Four days of camping out in the rough, looking for rustlers, but you're not tough enough to stand the thought of a little medicine."

"Ridiculous."

"Then stop caterwauling."

Alec sat up. "You run the rest of your life like this, nobody'd dare break your heart."

"Leave my heart out of this."

"What's left of it," Alec muttered under his breath.

"I'll get the hydrogen peroxide. It doesn't sting, if that's what you're afraid of," she called over her shoulder, aware that he was no longer protesting.

Moments later she returned with a small metal box. "What luck, a fully stocked first-aid kit was in the linen closet."

"One of my worst ideas." Alec was holding the photograph from the mantel. "How could you think this was me? My old man was in his late forties in this shot, nearly twenty years on my age."

"I had no idea how old our foreman was. I suppose I pictured you like Red."

"You really don't know more than a fence post about this operation or who runs it."

"We see that the ranch is in good hands. That's all I've needed to know."

"Long as the investment keeps paying off."

"The Rocker L is much more than that. Just because we're not out here regularly..."

"Regularly! I've been here three years and this is the first I've laid eyes on you. You thought I was forty-eight years old."

"It's been Jace's domain."

"Obviously."

The silence lay between them like the evening heat. She busied herself with opening the first-aid kit, fully expecting Alec to bolt. Instead he put his head back and sighed.

"I'm sorry," she murmured.

"You are one for apologies. What for this time?" he asked with his eyes closed.

"Even to a novice like me, it's obvious that four days and nights of tracking cattle rustlers is serious, exhausting work. I'm sorry I don't know more about the day-to-day operation because you're obviously in need of some real praise and appreciation. Forgive my ignorance."

Alec sat up. "Wait a minute. You think I need a pat on the back from you? You think I'm fishing for compliments?"

"Certainly. I'm sorry I don't know as much as you think I should. I'm sorry for snapping at you and being so defensive. Ranching is a tough job, thankless much of the time. That much I do know. I appreciate what you do for the ranch. It's only logical that you should want to hear that thanks from us."

"Us?"

"The Lydons."

He seemed at a loss for words. "Are you trying to make me feel guilty?"

"Is that what you think?"

He sank back into the cushion. "I don't have a clue what to think. What's clear as the brand on a steer gets turned inside out and you call it logic. Spring calves need branding, fall cattle need culling. That's logic."

"Forgive me. I never intended to start the bickering all over again."

"Baroness, you don't intend for a lot of things to happen. They just do. Four days out, hunting rustlers, napping against the trunk of a cottonwood tree with the rabbits and coyotes makes me desperate for a good meal and a good bed. I'm short on conversation, even shorter on temper. That's logic, too."

"Then we'll bandage this and be finished."

"It's none of my business whether you know beans about ranching," he added with a sigh.

Dory shifted to the arm of the chair. "But if I did, I would have known exactly how much effort's gone into catching the thieves. You wouldn't have had to lay it all out in front of me."

"You can stop worrying yourself to death over my need for fished-up compliments. I'm just doing what has to be done. I'm sorry for being short-tempered. That's about the best I can do in the way of an apology."

"Accept one from me, too. You're in pain because of me, exasperated because of me, probably wishing Jace had come out here, the way he was supposed to." She sighed. "Thanks to me, you've even had to give up your own bed."

"I haven't slept at the compound since Sunday. Wouldn't know what to do with a box spring and mattress anyway."

Dory shook her head and tipped the antiseptic solution into sterile gauze. She smiled to herself at the recollection of this chisel-jawed cowboy grabbing for her scarf.

"What?"

"Nothing."

"It's never *nothing* with you."

"Sit still and let's finish this."

"I've roped and branded panicked calves that were less work than figuring you out, Baroness."

Four

"**Y**ou have a colorful way with words," Dory replied.

"I'm out of words. Finish up so I can make dinner at the bunkhouse."

Dory gently wiped his shoulder. "Do you and the other hands go skinny-dipping a lot? Should I steer clear of the stream while I'm here?"

"Depends on where we're riding. I was rinsing off. There was more dust on me than a cow in July, that's all. Still is."

"I'll go to the main house so you can shower."

"Decent of you."

"I can be quite decent when pressed."

Alec shook his head. "Once this story gets out, it'll take the rest of the summer to live it down."

"That crevice was Jace's favorite hiding spot. That's probably why I sensed you were there."

"You been known to skinny-dip out there yourself?"

She smiled. "A long time ago."

"You looked to be giving it some thought this afternoon."

She dabbed.

"Ow! I was kidding."

"I was giving thought to how beautiful this is, how much peace there is out here. Serenity."

"Most days."

"Don't forget, even with my clothes on, you invaded my privacy, too. I'm not crazy about audiences, either, Alec, especially ones who are apt to quote everything they've heard, just to embarrass me." She wiped at the cut again.

He wrapped his fingers around her wrist in warning. "Lighten up."

"Hurt?"

"When you mean it to." He rotated her hand and stared at her fingernails. "What the heck color is that?"

Dory displayed her fingertips. "Luscious Red, if you must know. They're a mess now. Two nails are broken, the polish is chipped all over. My manicure's ruined from the rocks this afternoon."

"Ruined from pitching rocks at me. Somebody do them for you, back in Pennsylvania?"

She paused, then shrugged at the truth. "I have a manicurist, yes."

"A manicurist. Can't say I ever knew a woman who had a manicurist."

"It's a small luxury I treat myself to once in a while, nothing extravagant." She tried to ignore his enigmatic gaze. "You don't approve."

"Lord, woman, you do worry about what I think. It's not my place to approve. Wouldn't make a difference if I did or didn't. Watch it!" He tightened his grip as she touched his shoulder.

"You've spent an awful lot of time grabbing my wrists today."

"Self-preservation runs deep. Ow."

"I'm almost finished. I'm sorry, really."

"You said it wouldn't sting."

"I lied."

"Known to do that often?"

"Sometimes. When it gets the cooperation I need."

He gave her a hard, unreadable look, but she focused on nothing but the bruise. After a sharp breath, Alec muttered, "I'd love to see you in action when you've really got something to feel guilty about."

"Are we back to guilt?"

"You're tripping over it."

"I am not."

"Baroness, you're sunk in it up to your shins. Guilt over this wallop on my shoulder, guilt over your behavior in the crick, guilt over your ranch ignorance."

"You're the one who should be filled with guilt, spying on me, letting me carry on like a lovesick teenager."

His grimace turned to a grin. "Ever heard a cow bawl when the herd's culled and she loses her calf?"

"Do you compare everything to cattle?"

"Similarity's unmistakable. You were overdue for a good, hard cry. Nothing to be ashamed of, although I thought women like you unloaded their traumas on manicurists and hairdressers, or is it psychiatrists?"

"You're confusing Philadelphia with Beverly Hills."

"Women are as crazy on one coast as the other."

"Cows, Buck, cattle's all you know. Have you ever left Montana?"

"On occasion. This Tyler fellow, does he have a sense of humor?"

"Never mind about Tyler and my private life."

"Kept it to yourself all along? No wonder you let it rip this afternoon. I suppose you stored up all that bellyaching back East, having to be civil. A pile of rocks in the middle of the crick is as good a place as any to moon over a broken heart."

"As you know perfectly well, I thought I was alone."

He turned slightly. "With nothing but the wind to hear your caterwauling. So love made a fool of you. What else is love for?"

"Tyler Baldridge wouldn't know love if it jumped up and bit him."

"Few men would."

"Have you ever been in love?"

"Should be clear by now nobody'd put up with me."

She glared. "You're probably right."

"I heard bitter words in that crick. I wouldn't want to be in old Tyler's boots."

"He's overdue for a piece of my mind." She smiled. Alec let go of her wrist. "There's that grin again."

"I was trying to imagine Tyler in boots."

"Not the range-riding type? More the selfish, two-timing, egotistical snake type."

"Stop that."

"What?"

"Faking innocence, for one. For another, quoting everything I said."

"What I heard in the crick came from your gut. Words like that from a woman like you are enough to melt a man right down into his boots—if a man wore boots."

"My relationship with Tyler is history."

"I'll wager next month's pay, there's no turning you around once your mind's made up about something."

Next month's pay. She waited as the antiseptic dried, then looked over the packages of bandages in the open kit. "Alec, my relationship with Tyler is private, and at the moment very painful."

"Hell hath no fury..."

"It isn't funny." She opened the small butterfly bandages and wiped the cut with sterile gauze.

"Ow!" He grabbed her wrist again.

"Sorry. I'm almost finished."

"You said that," he muttered through gritted teeth. "I can put those things on myself."

"I promise to be gentle. Everything's clean," she murmured as she absently moved her fingers through the still-damp hair at his forehead. Almost imperceptibly Alec relaxed beneath her touch. He was quiet as she applied the first bandage.

The mood lightened—or deepened—Dory wasn't sure which. Alec's complexion darkened and he seemed to be holding his breath, making hers catch in the back of her throat. Whatever sarcasm or quip he'd been ready to hurl, disintegrated. Instead he sighed.

His look was as deep as the endless Montana landscape when he finally let go of her wrist. "I'll give you one last chance," he said.

Dory applied the second bandage with her finger-tips. "Trust me, Buck."

His features softened, and he continued to watch her as she opened the tiny tapes. With some annoyance, she brushed her palms on her thighs and continued. As she pressed the third one into place, his own breath caught.

"Hurt?"

"Not even close," he replied with his eyes closed.

One by one, she applied them, and with each her hands became less steady.

"I can feel you trembling, Baroness." He looked at her and made a show of folding his hands and resting them in his lap before closing his eyes again. "Get the *wound* closed nice and tight."

"We wouldn't want a scar on that perfect body," Dory replied as she covered the butterflies with a narrow patch of gauze. She pressed two dabs of tape at either end. "There," she chirped to break the spell that had descended on her. "That just about takes care of business."

Alec studied her. "What else is your business, Dory?"

She closed the kit. "I don't know what you mean."

"I'm speaking plain. What's brought a baroness whose only concern for the ranch is knowing the trust fund won't run dry, all the way out here in her brother's place?"

His words slapped her into attention. "You heard me this afternoon. I needed to get away. I needed someplace fresh, free of memories to do some thinking and clear my head."

"Old Tyler's ghost lurking on every corner of Sycamore Hill?"

She damned his perception, and damned the economics that had sent her. "You're overdue for that shower."

"I take it you're changing the subject."

"Yes. Even though you got an earful this afternoon, I value my privacy as much as you value your dignity."

He sat up slowly and began to button his shirt. "We'll save *values* for another discussion."

Dory stood up. "Another time."

Alec got to his feet and pulled her crumpled, stained square of silk from his pocket. "I'm afraid your dignity-saving scarf is ruined. I got blood all over it."

"Forget about it."

"It wasn't a present from Tyler?"

Dory glared. "If it were, you could toss it in a camp fire." She closed the kit. "By the way, I don't *caterwaul.*"

He grinned. "The heck you don't. Never in my life heard a woman carry on the way you can."

"I'm no more emotional than a man."

"East-of-the-Mississippi men, maybe."

"Montana cowboys are made of sterner stuff, I suppose."

"Barbed wire and rawhide, right to the core."

"Which I got more than a healthy glance at." To her surprise, he flushed again and she broke into a grin. "You can't imagine how silly you looked with only that pink rosebud scarf."

Alec abruptly turned. "You're giving me a pretty good idea. First aid's done. You're right, dinner needs checking."

"Barbed wire and rawhide, my foot. You can tease me till kingdom come but you can't take the tiniest reference to your own fiasco. Then again, what man could?''

"Bitter words," Alec repeated.

His unwavering glance made her look at her fingers, which she self-consciously brushed on her thighs. She displayed her fingernails. "My kingdom for a manicure."

Alec picked up the soggy towel he had held to his shoulder and started for the door. "Wouldn't you know it, I'm fresh out of polish and nail files."

Dory frowned. "I'm afraid I don't get it."

"Baroness, this ranch *is* your kingdom. If you're willing to give it up that easily, I'd even polish those luscious red fingernails of yours in trade."

Five

Dory left the foreman to his shower and headed resolutely across the grass courtyard for dinner with Red and Ginny O'Brien. Both the Lydon cottage and the bunkhouse faced the rambling, hundred-year-old log cabin that the Lydons had long ago modernized to provide housing for their ranch managers.

The domestic compound was sheltered from the open Montana landscape by full grown pines, cottonwoods and other trees that dappled it in shade. Hedges framed Ginny O'Brien's well-tended vegetable garden, laid out on the southeast corner. All of it was separated from the outbuildings—barns, equipment sheds, grain bins, stables—by the slope of the hills and the ever-present fencing.

Dory went to dinner. She ate with Red and Ginny and brought tears to their eyes over dessert as she described her introduction to the foreman. "All I wanted was a little privacy and a good cry. It's funny now," she added over their laughter, "but there wasn't much to laugh about at the time."

"I'm sorry about your broken engagement," Ginny replied, "but poor Alec."

Dory wagged her finger. "Don't give him any sympathy. The only thing that bothered him was my insisting that I treat the welt on his shoulder."

"He let you?"

"I didn't give him much choice."

When they'd finished, Dory followed Red into his den, which served as the Rocker L office. Over the desk was a framed sepia-toned photograph of Dory's grandfather, John Lydon, breaking a stallion in the corral where she'd so irresponsibly left the foreman's horse.

Next to it was a larger print of the second and third generation: Jack and Maggie Lydon with their children, the family who had carried on the legacy *in absentia*. Dory was in braids, propped on the corral; Jace was on horseback. She looked at both frames. "I was ten that summer. We were here for a month. Those were wonderful times."

Red sat in his swivel chair. "I look at those pictures every morning. Kind of inspires me. You look like your mother, Dory. I can't tell you how sorry I am she's in poor health."

"She does all right although the arthritis makes traveling difficult."

"When we lost your dad, I never thought she'd take the interest in this outfit the way he did. I expected the ranch to be sold out from under me."

"That's what we're trying to avoid now."

"She's proved me wrong more than once."

"She's a tough cookie, Red."

"I hope you've got some of Maggie in you. Are you ready to get down to business?"

"My mother's not one to shy away from tough decisions, especially when they come recommended by professionals. I'm only the emissary. You know what the accountants advised. Jace's been to New York and had all the papers drawn up."

Red put his fist to his heart. "We need a rancher interested in that range, not a mining company."

Dory sighed. "Red, I can only go by what the financial people see. Heartland Mining Company is offering a price that makes it possible for us to hold on to the rest of this."

The manager frowned. "Sell off a range, cut back on the herd. New York C.P.A.'s don't have Montana in their blood or cattle dust in their lungs."

"That's why we pay them to make business decisions. They're more rational than either you or my family."

"To their way of thinking, if we have less acreage, we need fewer men. We wouldn't need a foreman."

"So I understand." The image of that foreman bursting from the crevice at the creek pushed its way into her head. She saw Alec with the ice pack on his shoulder.

"McDowell's a good man, best we've had in some time."

She imagined how he'd look camped under a cottonwood, waiting for rustlers. Dory pulled a sheaf of papers from the briefcase at her feet and dismissed the unsettling images.

Although his expression was serious, Red leaned back in his chair. "Times are tough for every spread in the area. I wish like crazy I could tell you half a dozen ranchers are doing well enough to buy what we're contemplating selling, anybody but the coal people.''

''We all wish things were different, but they're not. Our accountants are forcing us to face reality. Here's the offer in writing.'' She handed him the contract. ''Heartland is interested in what amounts to the North Range.''

Red frowned. ''And paying twice what anyone else could possibly come up with. Strip-mining as a solution could only come from some accountant in a skyscraper who hadn't seen a sunset or an honest blade of grass in too long. Maggie's being mighty tough.''

''She won't admit it, but I know she's relieved that I'm doing the dirty work instead of her. Don't forget it's the answer to keeping the Rocker L solvent. Here's the information. It's mother's understanding that the geologists and mining engineers are putting together a package offer similar to what the next ranch over bought into. If we agree, they'll approach the abutters to the northwest. Is this still between us?''

''Rumors have been flying for months, all over the county. There's nobody thinks we're any more likely than the Bar J to give in to these guys.'' He handed back the contracts. ''You'll need to take a ride out there and look it over.''

''First thing tomorrow. Can you give me a tour?''

''I'm tied up with the Cattlemen's Association most of tomorrow.'' Red shook his head. ''If Alec hasn't gone back out, he's the one to give you a tour. He's been camped out there this week. Knows it like it was his. I hate to see the Rocker L cut to pieces after your grandfather spent his career building it up.''

"How easy will it be for him to get another foreman position?"

"Professionally, might do him some good. He seems content to hang on here, but he can do better than foreman. He's ready to take on a full spread, if he can find one, though I can't say there's much here, or the Dakotas. Texas maybe, Nebraska."

"Can we help?"

"I sure aim to. He's as capable as I am of running a whole outfit. As long as he's got your recommendation, we'll find him another spot. I'll see to it he lands on his feet."

"I appreciate the loyalty of both of you. For now, he's not to know."

"You're the boss." Red gave her a hard look.

"As I said, I'm just the emissary. Don't shoot the messenger."

The manager looked troubled. "Jack Lydon'd turn over in his grave, and your grandfather along with him, if they knew what was in the wind."

An hour later under more stars than she could count in a lifetime, Dory crossed the courtyard toward the guest cottage. She felt relieved to have shared the burden, relieved and confident.

Back East at Sycamore Hill the ranchers who made her life-style possible were simply colorful names on a payroll sheet: Red O'Brien, Alec McDowell, cowboys John Littlefeather, George Two Rivers, Boots Jensen. None seemed flesh-and-blood men with their own financial obligations and families to support, not until now.

There was work to be done and decisions to be made. The weight of it had already pushed thoughts of Tyler Baldridge to the back of her mind. Unfortunately it had also brought thoughts of Alec McDowell to the forefront.

The guest cottage porch light glowed under the overhang and the air was full of summer sounds. Across the way, music drifted from the bunkhouse. Low laughter followed. Dory bristled as she imagined the foreman regaling the cowboys with descriptions of her perseverance in the creek. She could hardly blame him.

A dog barked and she filled her lungs with the smells and sounds of her first Montana night. She prayed for the ability to remain dispassionate in the days ahead.

In no hurry to go into her empty quarters, Dory swung her leg over the log railing and propped herself against the posts. Her sense of well-being surprised her. There were too many decisions on her mind to call it contentment, too much ache in her heart to call it desire, but something almost physical sifted through her as she sighed.

A soft whistle rose above the distant bunkhouse music. Dory turned in the direction of the beech tree and squinted at the blackness beneath its great overhanging branches. A figure emerged and sauntered toward her. The foreman was coming from the barn.

The shadows accentuated his silhouette, but as he approached, the lamplight dissolved the monochromatic grays. His clothes were fresh. His shirt was blue flannel, his hair, a thatch of gold and wheat. The man was extraordinarily well put together.

Alec reached the porch steps as another round of laughter wafted in their direction. "Evening, Baroness."

"Buck. You're cleaner than when I last saw you."

He grinned. "I smell better, too."

Dory stayed perched on the railing. "How's your shoulder?"

"Well patched and a little stiff. But fine."

"I thought you might be in the bunkhouse causing all that laughter."

"What is it about me that's got you spooked? What makes you think I'd spill the beans and make you look foolish?"

She cocked her head. "A ranting and raving cattle baroness who doesn't know more than a fence post might be the perfect butt of some bunkhouse humor."

"True. Don't think it wouldn't bring some laughs. Trouble is, if I tell your story, I've got to tell mine, too." He shook his head. "This one's better kept between us."

"Too late. I already told Red and Ginny."

"Did they laugh themselves silly?"

"At me. I took the blame."

"That's where it belongs."

She turned to look at him. "Thanks!"

"It's my reputation I'm saving," he added lightly.

Dory smiled. "Beautiful night for a walk. Have you been at the barn?"

"A mare's lame. I was checking on her."

"I suppose I should apologize again for taking your horse."

"Wouldn't do your image any harm."

"I'm sorry."

"Good."

"Even sorrier I left him the way I did."

"See that it doesn't happen again. Sets a lousy example for the boys." His voice was soft.

"I want to ride tomorrow. I assume there's a free horse."

"Do you?" Annoyance at the way she phrased her request flickered through his features, but he climbed the steps toward her.

"Please." Each scrape of his boot on the risers made her heart dance.

He moved next to her and leaned back against the post. "Any place in particular?"

"That gully." She caught a whiff of after-shave lotion.

"North range?"

"Yes."

"Aiming to catch yourself some rustlers?"

"That's your job."

"Long ride out. You up to it?"

"I think so."

"From what I saw, you ride like the wind."

"I manage."

He studied her before gazing out into the dark.

"Why the scrutiny?"

"You tend to be one for understatement. Makes me wonder how well you manage, that's all. You've already said you're no stranger to stables. You ride Western back East?"

"Mostly English."

His eyes, darkened by the shadows, were full of questions. "You'll be needing Red to get you there."

Something stirred in her again, something that shifted from pleasant to wary as he leaned over, elbows propped on the rail within inches of her. "I asked him but he's tied up all day."

"I'll see one of the hands takes you out." Again, he looked into the dark. "Enjoy your supper?"

"Yes. I enjoyed the O'Briens."

"Red's a good man."

"We think so."

"We, meaning the Lydons."

It was impossible to read the tone of his voice. "The Lydons, yes. Do you find Red to be even-handed, fair?"

"Absolutely. He knows his cattle, knows this ranch from corner to corner."

"He said the same about you."

"He's taught me plenty."

"I gather you've taught him a few things, as well."

"Baroness, is this just small talk we're making?"

She hesitated. "Yes, of course."

"What are you after?"

Her heart jumped. "A look at the north range."

He nodded to himself. "Can't make it plainer than that."

"Plain seems to be the way you like things."

"I'm a cowboy. I live in a man's world. I get orders, I follow them. I need a job done, I give orders myself. Second-guessing a woman's the best way I know for a man to hang himself."

Six

Dory turned and faced the darkness. "Ginny says you pulled the garden up from scrabble."

"There's farming on my mother's side. Crops don't run a profit in this soil, of course."

"Not much does except cattle and mining."

"Cattle and mining." Alec's glance was sharp. "Oil and water. The two don't mix."

"A lot of people in this state feel otherwise."

"About mining?" He looked at the briefcase she'd propped against the railing.

"Yes."

He was slow in replying. "The economy runs in cycles. With luck, you weather the tough times. The Lydons and the Rocker L have been through slumps like these more than once."

"Red runs this ranch on common sense."

"Wish I had more of it myself."

"He tells me you've got plenty. According to him, you're ready to manage a ranch on your own."

"I'm content with the Rocker L for the time being."

"You could do better."

"We'll save this conversation for when you've learned something about ranching."

"I intend to learn plenty, Alec."

He studied her, then ran his hand over the railing. Next door the bunkhouse lights went out, and Dory watched the trees overhead as she fought the flutter his scrutiny produced.

With one last rub of the wood, Alec shifted his weight and stood up. "Past my bedtime. Days start early in these parts."

She, too, stood up and waited until he'd taken a few steps. "What about tomorrow?"

He paused. "I'll ask George to drive you out."

"If you're sleeping here tonight and going back to the range in the morning, I'd like to ride out with you, horseback. I could find my own way back."

He stuck his hands in his back pockets. "I've got business to tend to most of the morning."

"I can wait." She stood up straight and put only as much command in her voice as she thought she needed. "When might be a good time for you?"

Alec raised his eyebrows. "This your way of giving me orders?"

"If it comes to that."

"Understatement again?"

"Perhaps."

"You likely to get out there on the range and start caterwauling on me?"

"It's about as likely as you stripping down to my scarf."

He laughed, the deep, comfortable chuckle that sent gooseflesh under her sleeves. She straightened up so that he couldn't look down on her.

"You do meet a man eye-to-eye. If you want to ride out with me tomorrow, we'll ride. You're the boss."

"You don't need to make it sound like that."

"I've got no trouble with it. You seem to."

"I don't. Not at all." What she was having trouble with was the way he looked at her, the way he made her concentration dissolve, the curiosity he evoked. For her own peace of mind, it was imperative that he remain an anonymous employee, yet Dory could have lingered with him for hours more, under the stars, the June darkness and the huge Montana sky.

"I'll be back, late morning." He turned and started down the steps. "Can you take a piece of advice?"

"Certainly."

"While you're here, quit beating around the bush. It goes right over my head. Puts a man on edge, to boot. Maybe that's what fouled things up with Baldridge. Did the poor guy ever know what you wanted? Did you come right out and tell him?"

"Leave Tyler out of this. I'm asking for a look at the pasture, not your analysis."

"Take some lessons from your mother. When Maggie Lydon wants something, she makes it plain. If you aim to take her place, that's the first thing you've got to learn."

"I never intended to confuse you."

He stepped onto the grass and filled his chest with a yawn. "You seem to come by the ability naturally. Treacherous trait in a woman."

Dory waited until Alec had disappeared into the shadows again before she turned for the empty cottage. She went in and lingered in the living room, irritated by her own curiosity, which suddenly seemed insatiable.

She took the photograph from the mantel and looked at the father and son, not so different from her own father and brother. She glanced at the furnishings, the books and paraphernalia, his belongings. Alec McDowell.

On the way to her bedroom she stopped and flicked on the light to the room her parents had shared. The foreman had furnished the room with a queen-size bed and dresser, a rolltop desk and chair. There was a rumpled indentation in the bedspread, and she imagined Alec sitting on the edge of the bed, pulling off his range-riding clothes before he took a shower. She fought the urge to linger, then hurriedly snapped off the light when she remembered the room faced the bunkhouse. She finally readied for bed, knowing it would be a fitful sleep.

She awoke to heat, wind and a day well under way by the time she finished breakfast, studied the mound of papers she'd brought with her and set her priorities. She dressed in well-worn jeans, an open shirt of blue madras and the comfortable paddock boots she wore at Sycamore Hill. She refused to acknowledge that there might be a reason why she gave more attention than was necessary to her makeup and hair.

The compound was humming and for the first time she put the rest of the Rocker L names to faces. George Two Rivers and John Littlefeather, men nearly Red's age, were loading the pickup truck with spools of wire. Boots Jensen was at the wheel. She made small talk, asked what she hoped were knowledgeable questions and waved them off.

She looked at the sky, the endless undulating horizon so unlike the lush tree-heavy landscape of the Lydon estate in Pennsylvania. Harmless clouds sifted the sunlight as she walked toward the outbuildings.

As Dory approached the barn, Alec appeared, saddle in arms, at the open door of the stable. To support the weight, he leaned against the frame, boots crossed at the ankle. She avoided staring at the chaps he'd pulled over his jeans and looked instead at his Stetson cocked low, shading his eyes.

Her nerves danced. "Good morning," she tried as she reached him.

He acknowledged her with a lift of his chin. "We're about done with morning." He nodded over his shoulder. "Ginny's laid out a pile of sandwiches, brownies and thermoses of coffee in the lunch room for when the hands drift back. Take some if you're hungry. It's a long way out."

Dory shook her head. "I just finished."

"Lunch?"

"Breakfast."

His response was a slow, steady gaze.

"You don't approve."

"It's not my place to approve." He turned, shifted the saddle and called over his shoulder, "Follow me," as he walked the cement floored interior. He stopped at the tack room and put the saddle on a hay bale. "You'll cook out on the range without a hat. Wear Ginny's." He pulled a tan one from the shelf, rummaged through an open box and tossed a wrinkled bandanna at her. "Get this around your neck. Keeps down the dust."

"Thank you. I should have thought of it."

"Yes, you should have."

"I'll need chaps."

He pointed to the row of pegs. "You're probably taller than Boots. Give one of those a try."

She slid a pair over her own pants and tied them at the waist, then fixed the bandanna around her neck and propped the hat jauntily on her head. "How's that?" She anticipated a snappy comeback.

Instead, he heaved the saddle back up and muttered, "Better," as he lead her through the stable and out the rear where two quarter horses stood tethered in cross ties, waiting for their saddles. He shifted his onto the blanketed back of the mare. "The gelding's Sundance. This is Misty. She'll give you a comfortable ride."

Dory stepped next to Alec. "Thank you. May I assume your palpable lack of enthusiasm for this ride is because I ordered you along?"

"Palpable?"

"You've done nothing but growl at me since I walked over here."

Alec scowled.

"Had a bad morning? Does your shoulder still hurt?"

"It's my natural disposition."

The last of her self-consciousness evaporated. "Buck Naked, cranky cowboy."

"Damn."

Dory ignored the curse and the change in his expression and turned to the gelding next to Misty. "Sundance, I owe you an apology," she said to the horse as she stroked his neck. "I'll give you a good long session with the curry comb this afternoon to make up for my sloppy behavior yesterday." She pulled a carrot from her hip pocket and let the animal munch it off her open palm. "Cranky cowboys probably don't give you many of these."

When Sundance had taken the carrot, Dory turned back to Alec. "I'll brush him down when we get back."

"No need."

"Penitence. Sets a good example for the cowboys."

"They don't know how you left him."

"You haven't forgotten your lecture?"

"It wasn't a lecture."

"Reprimand, then. I can saddle my own horse, as well," she added as she walked over to Misty. "I'm Maggie Lydon's daughter. Surely you didn't think I expected to be waited on."

"After the way you left Sundance yesterday?"

"You know why I left the horse the way I did."

"Murdering, rapist burglars."

"Ah, a glimmer of humor." She fastened the girth of the saddle. Dory addressed the horse. "Misty, old girl, we may get him to lighten up, yet." She continued to ignore his irritability, checked the bridle, unhooked the cross tie and hoisted herself into the saddle. "Time's wasting."

Alec swung easily into his, tapped his hat low and urged his horse forward.

Dory stayed next to him at a walk. Across the paddock, the dust from the pickup truck was still settling. "Do the men enjoy working here?"

"Enjoy? Not much reason to be a cowhand, lest you love the work. Red's a good boss. He runs a clean, tight operation. Lydons pay fair wages."

"You know there's talk of computerizing the herds."

"No computer knows cattle the way a cowboy does."

"But if it made the operation more efficient—"

"Nobody knows your Rocker L herds the way Red does. No computer's going to keep fences mended and rustlers out."

"What about you, Alec? You're more in the business end of this operation than the cowboys. Do you know anything about computers?"

"Nothing I ever had to apply to ranching." He reined his horse toward the last corral gate and pointed at a distant pine-topped slope. "The north range runs over that rise and then along the pass to the pine ridge. Ready?"

"Been ready." Dory pushed her hat down to where it fit comfortably. She nudged Misty forward.

Still fretting over Alec, she watched him urge Sundance forward. Horse and rider were nearly one. Despite her resolve to keep him anonymous, she studied the way he moved, hoping a compliment might lighten the mood. She watched his hips as he rocked gently while the horse ambled. Flexed muscles beneath his chaps dragged her glance down along his thighs to his calves as he gripped the saddle when he needed control. A few minutes of this over open pasture made Dory grip her own saddle. As they passed a watering trough she trotted up next to him and forced her glance forward. "You ride like you were born in the saddle."

"Nearly was."

She cleared her throat. "Near here?"

"My father was foreman of a spread in Rosebud County. After he died, my mother moved my brother and me into Forsyth."

"Is she still there?"

"Yup."

"Your brother?"

"Teaches mathematics at Montana State."

"A college professor?"

"Yup. Lives in Bozeman. My mother hoped that if we went to college, we'd both be smart enough to pick something for a living besides other people's cows to knock our heads against."

"Did you finish?"

"B.S. in business management from the same school."

"No kidding."

"Tried it for a while. Always came back to the cows."

"Other people's."

"For now."

"And later?"

Alec watched a hawk. "Later never gets any closer in times like these."

"Red thinks you should be a ranch manager on your own."

"So you said."

"It would serve you well until you can set yourself up."

"Trying to get rid of me?"

Her cheeks flamed under the shade of the hat. "No."

"Well, to tell you the truth, I never thought it would take this long."

"To buy your own ranch?"

"Whatever." He nudged his horse forward, deliberately making it impossible for her to continue the conversation.

Seven

Dory lifted her hat and wiped her forehead. Behind her breastbone the physical swell of emotion made her breathing shallow. In an effort to clear her head, she nudged Misty into a canter. She passed Alec and headed for the distant hill.

Heat shimmered and hawks circled lazily. She forced her thoughts to the landscape and concentrated on her mission, until she lost herself in the endless, open range. Mindful of the heat and distance, she slowed to a walk, rocking gently in the saddle to the gait of the mare. She reined Misty in as she negotiated a slope. The grazing pasture finally narrowed and rose to the trail leading into the pines.

Dory waited and let Alec lead the way. He continued to guide his horse with an easy shift of muscle and bone. She watched his back as the wind teased his shirt.

They rode again in silence until Alec slowed Sundance at the top of the knoll. He turned and stood in the stirrups as he waited for her. "North range dead ahead."

"How many cows do we graze out here?"

"You don't know?"

Dory inhaled. "What I know is how much you disapprove of my ignorance."

"It's not my place—"

"Your place, your place. You throw that out at me once more and I'll knock you out of your saddle."

"Look—"

"No, you look. I'm sorry Red didn't have the time to bring me out here. I'm sorry I don't know more than I do, and I'm even sorrier I have to ask you for answers to questions you make clear I should already know." She searched his face for any hint of embarrassment. "I'm here to learn, even if it takes asking questions that make me look stupid."

"I never said you were stupid."

"Do you think I need you to put it into words?"

"Baroness—"

"Never mind. Just answer my question."

Alec jammed his finger in the direction of the distant cattle barely visible on the open range. "You've got nearly eight hundred head, there and farther below. Can't be seen from here."

"And neither can the rustlers and their trucks?"

Alec nodded.

"Thank you." She walked her horse forward, the silence broken only by the wind and the creak of saddle leather. Off to the south a log cabin backed onto another hillock. There was a trace of a corral and a roofless shed. As she stood up in her stirrups for a better look, Alec came up beside her. "Why didn't you camp out in there?"

"Too obvious."

"Jace and I begged to sleep out there one summer. I thought it would be the ultimate adventure."

"Was it?"

"My father insisted it was too far from the ranch, so we never got the chance. It's an old homestead, as I recall."

"Was once."

"My grandfather bought it years ago, right?"

"Long time back. John Lydon picked up this parcel from a struggling rancher during the Depression." From under his hat, his glance was penetrating.

"Another fact I should have known?"

"No."

"At any rate, it doesn't have much sentimental significance for us," Dory replied.

"Would that make a difference?"

She felt herself blush. "In what?"

"You tell me."

"Some would say there's no place for sentiment in this business. And others would say there's not much else to recommend ranching," Dory replied, playing the devil's advocate. She swung her leg over the saddle and dismounted.

"We've got a ways to go."

She tied Misty to the closest pine. "My legs need stretching. Riding this far takes more work than I remembered."

She could feel the heat of Alec's stare as she left him and walked from the shade into the sun. With her hat in her hand, she put her face to the wind and shook out her hair. She still ached inside and it was the ache that fueled her frustration. It had been with her all morning, the ache to cheer the recalcitrant cowboy, to change his disposition, to understand him.

Her yearning burned. No matter where she looked, no matter what she forced herself to concentrate on, his glance, his tacit disapproval broke her concentration, shredded her good intentions. For no apparent reason, she ached for his approval. Dory shook her head again as if she could rid herself of the sudden revelation. His approval! She didn't need approval from any man.

Without ceremony, she sat on the hillside and looked down at the remains of the homestead. Behind her one of the horses whinnied as she pulled her hair up, off her neck in an effort to cool herself. Less than a minute passed.

"You going to lie out there all day and fry yourself?" he called.

"You never know. I might just lie out here till the cows come home."

Alec came to her and she glanced at the faded jeans that wrapped his hips above the chaps. She enjoyed the sliver of pleasure. When she didn't move, he sat down next to her.

"That expression refers to dairy herds."

"It suits this situation." She leaned back on her elbows and purposely looked at him. "Don't get too close, Buck. I've got a nice horse and a beautiful day. This is gorgeous country. I'm in a very good mood. I'd hate for some of it to rub off on you."

"Sorry," he muttered.

"For how much?"

"You think you're getting a raw deal."

"I am getting a raw deal."

"Then I'm sorry."

Dory waited but nothing followed. She turned her attention back to the cabin. "From the minute I arrived at the stable, you made it very clear that you didn't want to bring me out here. This whole ride was an imposition. It still is."

He looked at his fingernails. "I suppose my manners can be less than civilized."

"It was a simple request."

"And here I am." He chewed a blade of grass.

"Here you are—dragged kicking and screaming into the sunlight."

He focused on a drifting cloud, then smiled ruefully. "Am I as bad as all that?"

"You wouldn't be asking if you didn't suspect that you are."

"Okay, I apologize."

"Have I done more to offend you? Is there something I can patch up verbally?"

"Nothing needs patching."

They sat side by side in a silence screaming to be broken. He finally turned to her. "Just as well I came along. It settled my curiosity some."

"About what?"

"How you handle yourself in the saddle." He rubbed his sleeve across his forehead.

"Well?"

"Well what?"

"Come on, Buck, would it kill you to hand out one compliment? Do I pass inspection—for an eastern greenhorn?"

"Not bad."

"But you can't bring yourself to tell me I ride well enough to make up for some of the rest of my ignorance."

His green gaze was intense, deepened by the shadow from his hat brim. "You look good in the saddle. Damn good."

Dory's cheeks flamed at the thought that he might have been watching—and reacting—to her riding as she'd been to his. "Thanks."

"The way I imagined you would," he added softly as he leaned forward.

She licked her lower lip in an effort to moisten what was suddenly parched. "Buck?"

Alec smiled slowly with a lingering glance in complete contrast to everything she'd endured so far. "Simple truth is, it takes a lot less effort to enjoy your company than to fight it."

"That's what you've been doing?"

"Fighting like a roped steer, since you ambled into my stable today." He looked at his hand, then slowly, deliberately, traced the flush from her cheek to the lobe of her ear. "Baroness, you don't seem any more comfortable with a compliment than you do with a complaint."

The dry wind intensified the pinpoints of desire dancing over her. His bandanna fluttered at his throat. When her hair tumbled across her temple, Alec tucked it behind her ear, still teasing her flesh with his index finger. As he paused, she brought her own hand to the side of her face. Her fingertips found his hand.

Like August prairie grass under a discarded match, her ache, the yearning, ignited into desire. She closed her eyes so he couldn't read them. With equal pressure, his hand and hers moved to her shoulder. She could feel his warmth right through the madras. He opened his fingers. Each movement continued to be excruciatingly deliberate.

"I'm sorry. I was fishing for a compliment," she murmured.

"You look pleased with what you got. I could offer more."

"I know," she whispered.

"So could you, Dory."

"It's a tempting offer." She opened her eyes, and with reluctance she hoped wasn't evident, moved her hand from over his.

"An offer to make us both sorry," he added. He took his hat off and ostensibly examined the band. "If you were any other woman—"

"But I'm not." There was no question in her voice.

"Not even close." He jammed his hat back on his head and cleared his throat. "You're worse than a burr under a saddle."

There was pleasure in the simple act of watching him fight his own emotions. There was also relief. It took the emphasis off what she was fighting.

"You're a hard man to read, Alec."

"I'm a simple man with simple needs. I supervise cowhands and help to manage a ranch. I mean to have my own someday. There's little I love more than this."

Guilt and regret mingled with her still simmering desire. They were quiet. Dory looked out at the lay of the land and mentally reminded herself of exactly why she had ridden out. In the guest cottage, filed in her briefcase with other pertinent papers, were maps of all the proposed acreage Heartland Mining Company wanted, acreage that lay out in front of her.

She dragged her thoughts back to business. "Isn't there an access road out here?"

"Over that rise. Can't see it. Except in a still night, can't hear the whine of a truck out there, either."

"That's how the rustlers get here?"

"Easy as pie when the wind's up."

Dory pointed to a streambed between them and the scattered herd, which would serve as the southern boundary between the Rocker L and the coal exploration. "Same creek as our skinny-dipping spot?"

"Same one. Sundance and I just followed it over that rise and down to where it deepens out."

"To where I suddenly appeared."

"Spitting fire."

She smiled. "Caterwauling."

"That, too. Got it all out of your system?"

Dory looked out around her. "You know, Alec, I really have. There's too much out here to learn, too much to concentrate on to dwell on the rotten behavior of some man. Dwelling on any man's a waste of my time." She touched her heart.

Eight

Dory studied the pines. As the geologists, the mining engineers and even her family had said, the parcel was easily sliced from the ranch. The natural ridge and the stand of ponderosa that they had crossed would shield the strip-mining operation from view. What noise the operation made would drift with the wind this far from the compound. She turned to search out the herd.

"...Eventually," Alec was saying. "You with me, Dory?"

"I'm sorry. I was thinking about the cows. What did you say?"

Alec pointed to the stream. "Nothing much. It's hardly more than a trickle come high summer. Floods every spring. Turns back behind us and runs up to the Musselshell, eventually."

Teasing Alec kept her mind on track. "Ever strip down out here?"

He wiped his forehead with his sleeve. "You ever going to let up?"

Dory smiled. The smile broke into a grin and she put her hand back on his arm as she started to laugh. "You looked so startled, at a loss."

He brought his hands down and muttered, "Never mind how I looked."

"You don't strike me as someone who often loses control of a situation."

"I try hard not to get caught with my pants down."

"Figuratively, as well."

"Figuratively, most of all." He turned and studied her bandanna first, then the hair loose around her face.

The command she felt whenever she teased him dissolved. Words stuck in her throat. Along her neck, and at her temple, she could feel her pulse throb. She still ached for him to touch her. She was still terrified he would.

"I'm a burr under your saddle?"

"And then some. You come out here using ten dollar words for five dollar feelings, swinging a briefcase full of god-knows-what. You insist you're here to mend your heart you let some stiff-necked, green-horn crush under his boot. Sorry, under his shoe." He sat up straight and inched away from her.

"I don't need your five dollar analysis of my ten dollar problems. Hasn't any woman ever challenged your common sense?" His uneasy look made her smile. "There's got to be someone who's driven you to caterwauling."

"I'm not one to give any woman the chance. Never mind. We were talking about this territory."

"Not the tender territory in there, under your ribs." She pointed to his chest.

He covered his shirt buttons as if he'd felt her fingertip. "Nothing tender in there. Nothing but gristle and bone."

"Rusted horseshoes where your heart should be?"

"All wrapped up in baling wire."

Dory's ears burned. His voice was pure syrup, yet there wasn't a hint of flirtation in it. He left her with the bizarre feeling that she was misinterpreting his sexual innuendos. He looked intrigued, curious, and not a little irritated.

She pointed down the hill. "Tell me about that place, the homestead. Do we ever use it?"

"If we're branding out here and the weather turns miserable, we'll bunk in it, after we chase the critters out."

"Any snakes?"

"Just the slithery kind. No selfish, two-timing, egotistical ones."

"You're referring to Tyler again. I wish you'd stop that."

"Lady, you're a force to be reckoned with. I'm just curious as to what that man had that could turn you to jelly."

"I've asked myself the same question. It seems I found the cure, finally. Except when you bring him up, I haven't given him a thought. There's not much out here to remind me he even exists."

"All that carrying on must have done you some good." He pulled his knees up and cocked his hat back. " 'Two-timing, egotistical snake.' Can't imagine you wouldn't be more than enough for a man to handle, egotistical or otherwise," he said softly. "What was it this morning, 'palpable lack of enthusiasm'? You've got a way with words even when you muddy up any chance of getting the meaning."

"I haven't muddied up a thing."

"Except my common sense. What's Baldridge do—besides take you for granted?"

"Tyler's a trust officer in a Philadelphia bank."

"Tyler Baldridge. Sounds like East Coast money. Any numbers after it? Tyler the Fifth?"

"Just Junior. Alec McDowell's not your run-of-the-mill cowboy name. Not like Buck Naked." She grinned at him.

Alec's expression hardened. "My great-grandfather was a Scot, a crofter sick of breaking his back for other farmers in the lowlands. He immigrated to Ohio and just kept pushing west."

"And three generations later, you're breaking your back for other people."

"Part of the game plan."

She watched the herd. "Your own ranch, eventually."

"Eventually." He turned to the horizon.

"I don't mean to make you uncomfortable. We had enough of that yesterday." She looked down the hill. "Let's get the subject back on track. Where's your campsite?"

"About another mile into the range, beyond the cabin and up in those pines. It gave me a good view of the access road and the wind's right for hearing the whine of a truck climbing the hill."

"Or the bark of a collie?"

"Exactly."

"Are they apt to strike again so soon?"

"So far I haven't been able to make heads or tails of their game plan. Small-time operation's likely to take a couple head at a time. No more."

"A few that won't be missed, as you said."

"They figure we're less apt to prosecute. Honorable rustlers have even been known to leave any they suspect might be a kid's 4-H project."

"Honor among thieves."

"Occasionally."

"Besides the danger, it must have been wonderful out here under the stars."

"Gets cold. Hard bed."

"That's the romance of it all. Lying out here under the stars dreaming your dreams."

"My dreams?"

"Of that ranch you'll buy, or some woman you've got an eye on. How refreshing the skinny-dipping was, till I ruined it." She shrugged. "Whatever it is that cowboys think about."

Alec shoved his hat back.

"Have I said something?"

He shook his head. "Before you leave the ranch I mean to figure out how it is that you do this."

"Do what?"

"I'll be damned if I have a word for it. You talk ranching—smart as a whip one minute, run ignorance up the flagpole the next. Just when I think you're showing an interest, just when I think I can see the potential, you get me all twisted around like last year's baling wire."

"Am I asking stupid questions?"

"They aren't stupid. It's just hard to figure out a woman who, in the middle of an explanation of cattle rustling or stream flooding, asks a question that reminds a man he got caught buck naked in front of her.''

''Since I bared my soul at the creek, I guess I still feel the need to keep you a little off balance.''

''You're a grown woman with an obvious mind—and will—of your own.''

''Why are you laying this all out for me?''

He raised one eyebrow. ''In case you get to feeling like a grown woman with a will of her own. Horse throws you, the best cure—''

''Is to get back on the horse. You're being awfully presumptuous, Alec.''

''There's a look in your eye that's pure challenge. Makes a foreman forget his place.''

She laughed. ''I'm sorry you don't like my look. If I've done something—''

''Baroness, that look could melt a man into his boots.''

Nine

Dory rubbed her cramped legs. Well in front of them, a flock of birds fluttered off the turf and out of the way of whatever had startled them. With some effort, Alec put his hand in his jeans' pocket and pulled out a rectangle of tissue paper. He handed it to her.

She opened it and held up a pink silk scarf, accentuated with cabbage roses. "Alec."

"Couldn't find one with just the buds on it."

"You've had this with you all this time? Even when you were so nasty?"

"I haven't been nasty."

"You've been recalcitrant, intractable and cantankerous since I met you at the stables."

"Twenty dollar words."

"You've been a total pain in the saddle. Is that better?"

"I get your point."

"Wonderful. Unfortunately, I don't get yours. You're difficult and tight-lipped for hours, then within a breath of kissing me."

"Was that what I was doing?"

"It certainly felt like it."

"Temporary insanity."

She held up the silk so that the breeze fluttered it. "You didn't need to replace my scarf. It was just as much my fault."

"I've got a need to square things."

"This is beautiful. I like this one better."

"Don't make too much of it."

She grinned at him. "We wouldn't want you all embarrassed and tongue-tied again."

"I'm just clearing the debt."

"It was thoughtful, whether you meant it to be or not." She put her face to the wind and closed her eyes again, hot and dusty, relaxed and invigorated.

There were as many aspects to Alec McDowell's personality as there were shadows on the creek ledge. Almost like facets, she thought. One minute words would bounce off him, the next he'd absorb everything she said. He could be diamond bright or soft as amber.

She wouldn't—couldn't—respond to his passes, yet that was irrelevant. The dead spot, the hollow in her heart left by her ex-fiancé, was healing. After weeks of numbing misery, she was coming back to life and what better place than the beloved open spaces of the Rocker L.

She was capable of feeling. For another long moment she sat in the grass and let the revelation wash over her. She was physically stirred by all that was hers, and confused by all that wasn't. What's more, she suspected the cowboy was, too.

Dory watched the undulating field as the grass bent in drifts driven by the wind as she fantasized. Perhaps the mission that had brought her to Montana would end perfectly. After the sale of the parcel, Alec would be hired as ranch manager on a neighboring spread. They'd celebrate the promotion and part with appreciation as he moved closer to his own dream.

She looked down at the cabin below them. There would be moonlight, the distant lowing of cattle and the hard strong body she'd already glimpsed. There'd be humor, more small talk, revelation. She and Alec would stoke their mutual desire until they erased all thought, until they locked the world out and shared nothing but pleasure, deep enough to satiate them. She'd sleep in the cowboy's arms until dawn and watch the sun rise over—

"Too hot out here. You're flushed even under the hat."

Dory blinked and wiped her brow again. She was a grown woman all right, but it was her imagination that had a mind of its own. "You're right," she answered hastily.

"We've got more riding to do," he muttered as he got to his feet and brushed dust from his shirt.

Dory stretched and watched him go back to the horses. Her fantasy had no more substance than the whiffs of clouds teasing the horizon. In too many ways her life was no more substantial than those clouds, the cowboy no more than a temporary diversion.

As soon as they'd mounted, Alec dug his heels into the gelding's flanks and lit out over the pasture. Dory followed and together they kept up the pace across the

open expanse until they reached the natural finish line
of the stream. Alec pointed out the access road and the
mended fencing. "Rich land out here. This is all
overburden."

"Coal beds underneath."

"Too rough for farming, of course, a plough would
peel it right back to nothing. All this was meant for
cattle."

"Even with the streambeds drying up every summer?"

"Coal's a natural aquifer, twenty-five percent water under our horses."

"I knew that, of course."

"Just assumed you would."

Again, the shadow cast by his hat kept Dory from
seeing his expression. Since there wasn't any sarcasm
in his voice, she didn't take offense. "Our accountants keep pointing out that rich land or not, the eight
hundred Herefords growing fat on this grass won't
bring the prices we need to see a profit."

"They'll be off to the Nebraska feed lots in October. If your mother chooses, we can reduce the herd
to studs and heifers and lease the land next spring."

"For someone else's cattle."

"We've had a wet spring, the range is greener than
it's been for the past three years. The Rocker L could
support another thousand head if we open the west
side of what's now the breeding pasture."

"I know Red recommends it, but we tried it five
years ago, before you were hired. It was a financial
disaster."

"Those were different conditions. Down here the
north range was hardscrabble, mostly prickly pear
from lack of rain. Now the flats are healthy."

"And what if we lease the range and wind up with a dry winter and spring? This time next year we'll have two thousand head of other people's cattle grazing on land that can't support them."

"You didn't get to be a cattle baroness without Lydons taking risks before you. Take a good look. The range is green."

"Green as you think I am about ranching, I suppose."

"You're a fast learner. Better than that—" He dropped his voice.

"I can't hear you."

"Just as well."

"Alec McDowell, if that was another compliment you're swallowing, you'd better shout it. You owe me."

"I was going to say that you listen. You're not afraid to admit when you need answers."

She cocked her hat and grinned deliberately as she imitated his drawl. "Might be, cowboy, what you've got to say's worth hearing."

"Maybe so."

"Otherwise no Lydon would have hired you in the first place." They shared a glance. "Now finish what you were saying about the lease arrangement."

"There are plenty of ranchers get a dry season or two and they're looking to farm out their stock. Both parties profit when it's handled right. It's one solution. There's others to consider."

"I'd like to hear them all."

"Then stick around awhile. Spend a season out here, get to know what it takes to make this run."

"I have obligations."

"This ought to be one of them. Make it more than a family investment. Put your heart into it. Ranching won't break it, like a man will."

Her lips parted, but she swallowed her response.

Alec waved his hand. "Not in the same way, at least. While you're sitting on that mare, doing all that listening, here's some more advice you never asked for. Keep that East Coast banker out of your system. Clear that pretty head of yours. You don't need me to tell you that the Rocker L's going to need a strong hand in the years coming up. It could do with your touch, as much as your brother's, Dory."

Dory. Inexplicably, hearing her name in his deep, even voice unleashed a rush of adrenaline. High in the saddle, under the vast sky and the afternoon heat, her heart thundered. "I intend to, of course, although I have other concerns at home."

"Home," he repeated. "That would be Sycamore Hill."

"I have a business."

"There's few businesses can compare to this. While you're here, at least, concentrate on everything that's yours. Put your heart into the ranch."

For the moment she chose to concentrate on the way he sat in the saddle and the cut of his shirt across his back. She watched him drum his thigh with the fingers of his left hand. "You really love this place, don't you?"

"Maybe more than any of you."

Dory let the silence wash over them. Alec patted Sundance and watched a hawk sailing over them.

"There's a lot to be learned," she said finally.

"How long'll you be here?"

"I fly out Monday afternoon."

"Not much time." He reined his horse around toward the compound. "Barely enough to finish this crash course and make Maggie proud."

Dory nudged Misty forward and tried not to think about her mother. Maggie Lydon would have been anything but proud if she could have read her daughter's mind.

Ten

Dory pressed Misty to follow the edge of the meandering stream. Without asking, she forded it and
nudged the mare closer to the grazing cattle, most of
which ignored her.

The range was hot, musty with the smell of cattle
and dust. She smiled as she spotted the brand on each
hip. The Rocker L was hers as much as anyone's. With
expert horsemanship, she approached the cattle at a
walk. Whether Alec approved or not was impossible
to tell from his expression.

For the next hour she asked every question that
came to her, from calving to branding. She asked
about inoculations, castration and breeding. She
asked about seasonal work and hiring practices, about
the jobs handed out to the cowboys and the condition
of the bunkhouse.

Not only was Alec an expert on range management, he lost her completely when he discussed the benefits of the government crop reduction programs and their acres of winter wheat. From there he moved into the health plan and medical benefits that came with Rocker L employment and finally bond investment for retirement.

"It's a far cry from a John Wayne movie," she said.

"Always was."

She sat up in the saddle and took a final look at the landscape and the lowering sun. "Alec, thank you for bringing me out here."

"You're full of surprises. I hadn't planned on answering so many questions."

"That's why I wanted you to give me the tour."

"It wasn't my charming disposition?"

"Your disposition's improved since this morning."

"Must be the scenery." He smiled at her. "It's about time you got around to sticking your nose in your own business."

"It is my ranch."

"Remember that."

"I intend to. It's time I headed back. I know the way. You can go on over to your campsite."

He pointed at the first rise. "Through there and along the stream to start. Trail's marked. Misty knows where dinner's set."

"Horse sense." She patted the mare's neck. "Will I see you again before I go back to Philadelphia?"

"Depends on the nights out here. Probably not, unless the weather turns. Might be just as well," he added softly.

"I won't be throwing any more rocks."

"Might help if you did."

"Is there a compliment in there somewhere?"

He sighed. "You're a damned appealing woman. Under other circumstances— You'd make a good boss, if it came to that."

And because of what I'm here to do, I'm about to lay you off entirely. Wrapped in guilt, she nudged the horse closer and put out her hand. "Thank you. If this is goodbye, then I'll tell you now how much I appreciate your patience. Thanks, Buck."

He shook her hand. "My pleasure."

"I hope you get that ranch before too long."

He tipped his hat. "I mean to. Say hello to Jace."

"I will." She saw the kiss coming. Alec leaned in the saddle and put out his hand. The easy motion drew her in and without more than a shift of her boot to the stirrup, she leaned over. He cocked his head and pulled off his hat, then took hers, as well.

The moment their lips brushed, desire bubbled. She kissed him back, lightly, and savored the warmth and the sweet tingle. "Alec?"

"Melt a man into his boots," he said as he put the Stetson back on her head.

She tried to keep the moment light. "So long, cowboy. I'd better ride off into the sunset before I get a hankering to stick around the camp fire."

"You'd be more than welcome."

His invitation did devilish things to her imagination. She reined in the horse. "Keep them cows safe, hear?"

"Yes, Ma'am." He wiped his forehead with the back of his sleeve and put his hat on.

"So long, Buck."

"So long, Baroness."

Fully aware that he was watching her retreat, Dory nudged Misty and cantered across the Montana range toward home.

Part of Dory wished she'd never ridden out. It would be hard to give up this range to anybody else, let alone a mining company. It was a decision better made in the sterile offices of the Lydon's New York accountants.

She'd gone a mile or two, over the rise and through the ponderosa that formed the natural boundary between ranges, when the sound of horse's hooves clattering behind her made her turn. In a cloud of dust, Sundance and his handsome rider were galloping up behind her.

When she finally reined Misty to a stop, she sat panting with her hand on her heart. "You scared the daylights out of me."

"I had no business letting you ride back alone. There's men out here up to no good."

"Alec, they're after the herd, miles in the opposite direction."

"You're my responsibility."

"This isn't necessary."

"Cowboy code, ma'am. I aim to see you home."

She took time to look at him, not at all sure she wanted to talk him out of it. "Then see me home."

"I'll eat at the bunkhouse. Food's a darn sight better than what I pull out of cans. I'll drive back and trailer the horse. Be better to have a truck out here, anyway." This time they cantered off together.

As they returned to the compound and came over the last hillock, the cowhands emerged from the barn.

As Dory rode into the corral, she greeted Boots Jensen and George Two Rivers.

"Where you boys off to?" Alec asked as he dismounted.

Boots nodded toward the east. "Got to take these stakes out to the south range. Be back in twenty minutes, if I'm needed."

Dory slid from her saddle. "Any room for me?"

Still in his saddle, Alec shook his head. "Haven't you had enough?"

"I've got to make up for lost time."

Alec looked back at Boots. "Watch out for this Lydon, she'll question you—"

"Till the cows come home," Dory threw in.

Boots grinned. "Ma'am, I'd be proud to show you what we built."

Dory looked back at Alec. "Leave the horses. I'll keep my word and groom them when we get back."

Alec cocked his hat. "I appreciate your offer. George and I'll tend to the horses. You go on out. A lesson from Boots in fence-mending's more important."

Dory followed the cowhand to his pickup truck, aware that Alec's expression was pure satisfaction. For reasons she tried not to dwell on, she cared about his opinion.

The moment she entered the cab of the pickup truck, the cowhand regaled her with descriptions of the miles of fencing that crisscrossed the ranch and the importance of keeping it in working order. The middle-aged fence mender explained the necessity for top quality barbed wire and the importance of constant vigilance. The truck rumbled over the rutted trail, bordered by examples. When Boots stopped, Dory helped slide the posts from the truck bed and pile them for the next day's work.

Thirty minutes later, they returned by way of the calving shed and windbreak. "Another of my designs," he added proudly. "Me and the foreman, that is. Alec's got a way with the math and the figuring. I got a way with the hammer and nails." He chuckled at his joke.

Dory insisted on a tour of the area, as well, as much to continue her crash course in ranching as to mollify her cowhand.

"Misery all around—for cows and cowboys—if them calves're born in mean weather. And, ma'am, any spring can be mean. Wind could bite your ears off, ground hard as stone, like to freeze us all, calves included. This here lean-to breaks up the wind, gives them mothers a little comfort. Us, too, tough as we are," he added with a wink.

"You're a tough bunch and I think that's just the way you like it."

"Suits us."

"You do good work."

"We aim to please."

After a tour of the shed designed for efficiency and protection, Boots continued his description of the spring nights and the vigilance required to bring the calves safely into the world. "We've got ourselves ninety-six this season, all branded and out with their mothers. 'Course you know that."

"I've just come back from the north range." She looked across at the corral where Sundance and Misty—groomed and free of their saddles—stood.

"'Course you know I spotted signs of rustlin' out there. Didn't lose but one or two. That's the way them bandits work. Take only what you won't miss for a while. Slick fellows. Words already out, Alec's on to them. He's got the sheriff on the case.''

''Part of the problem is the lay of the land. That range is a natural valley, much easier to reach, and see, from the access road than from the ranch.''

''True enough. Words also out coal people been sniffin' around out there.''

Dory turned and looked at her employee. ''What have you heard?''

''Offers are juicy. Ain't a rancher can match what them mineral men'll pay. Old Maggie—'' He stopped and flushed into his scalp. ''Excuse me. Mrs. Ly-don'll get pressured one day soon.''

''Should she consider it?''

''Selling off the range? Ain't my decision. Mineral people'd have you believe there's nothin' to working side by side with them.''

''Do you agree, Boots?''

''No, but these is hardscrabble times. They say mining don't hurt the land.''

''Reclamation?''

''Yup. When they're done stripping out the coal, they kind of put the land back the way it was.''

''So I understand.'' She began to walk with the cowboy at her side.

''Makes a racket above ground, but there'd be nothing but the cows to hear it. 'Course it ain't my decision.''

Dory waved him off with a thanks for the tour and headed for her long overdue shower. Technically, it hadn't been her decision, either.

She sighed and hurried toward the guest cottage, grateful for the shade of the overhanging beech between the barn and the houses. As she rounded Ginny's vegetable garden, she caught sight of the foreman. Alec was coming out of his cottage. His face was flushed and his expression was pure fury.

Eleven

He was still as much in need of a shower as she, and every bit as handsome as when she'd left him at the corral. As if he sensed her stare, he turned sharply, startled, and softened his expression. She watched him take a deep breath.

"Are you all right?" she asked as she reached him. "You looked ready to let somebody have it."

"Fine. Never better." Alec gave her a searching look, then held up the metal container. "I didn't know how long you'd be, so I let myself in to get the first-aid kit."

"It's your home, Alec."

He shrugged. "Yours, too. Anyway, my bandage needs changing."

"I'll be happy to do it for you."

"I gave that considerable thought."

"It shouldn't sting anymore. You know you can trust me."

The foreman arched one eyebrow. "Trust. Now there's a word got more meanings than you can shake a stick at."

"I don't understand."

"Never mind. In this case, can't say as I trust myself."

Dory raised her face to the shower spray and let the warm water sluice over her. Lord, how the man could flirt. At least it felt like flirting. Weren't a racing heart and damp palms proof of that?

She poured shampoo into her hair and scrubbed her scalp. The man could change dispositions with the turn of a breeze and criticize. They paid him well for that critical eye. She scrubbed until the suds were gone, then turned around and rinsed. Not that it should have been turned on her. Her skin was tight, her breasts gooseflesh.

Alec McDowell had a way of cutting right to the bone, right to the heart of anything he considered. Unconsciously, Dory put her hand over her own heart and felt the steady thumping beneath her fingers. The thin, razor line of pain was gone. In its place was warmth. She pressed her fingertips to her breastbone. The spot was no bigger than an ember, but the glow was steady and the heat, comforting.

She rubbed herself with a fresh towel, reveling in the sensation. When had she last felt alive? How long had it been since her body had responded to anything but the weight of grief and the ache of rejection? She grinned as she dried her hair.

She'd put on a clean pair of khakis and a fresh oversized green T-shirt lined in pink. The new scarf, wound and knotted, lay at her throat. "Nice touch," she murmured as she left the bedroom.

Once she'd pulled her briefcase into her lap, Dory hummed as she riffled through the contents in search of the Heartland file. She opened the geological survey map on the couch and ran her finger over the boundary of the Rocker L.

"Take the money and run," she said as she thought of Boots. She pulled out the bill of sale with her mother's signature and skimmed the endless legalese that would bind the agreement once she delivered the document Monday morning. The ember deep under her ribs began to burn. She thought of Alec and his devotion to the ranch. Dory looked at her watch.

It was early evening eastern standard time. Sycamore Hill on a Saturday was apt to be full of Jace's tennis group or an impromptu party of her mother's friends.

It was not the best time to call home and express her doubts about the sale. Even under ideal circumstances, they'd think she was over her head. Business decisions such as these were made in New York, by the accountants, not the Johnny-come-lately, dewy-eyed daughter who was leading with her heart.

Since Alec hadn't made any overtures where dinner was concerned, she pulled together a light supper and ate on the porch, thinking about her family. None of the Lydons, any more than she, thought about the effort it took to keep the ranch going, or the personalities involved. Even Maggie's priority was a healthy balance sheet at the end of each fiscal year.

As soon as she finished, she went in search of Red O'Brien. George Two Rivers was coming from the ranch house with the day's mail. "You missed him. He and Ginny went into Swenson for pizza and a movie. Need some help?"

"No thanks. I wanted his advice on a few things, but it can wait till tomorrow. I think I'll wander around, if nobody minds."

He tipped his hat. "No, ma'am. It's yours to wander."

In the dwindling daylight she headed to the barns with the sun low and the temperature more comfortable. She walked through the corral and into the stable where the lame horse stood in the only occupied stall. The air was ripe with the familiar musk of horses, fresh hay and liniment.

Dory rubbed the mare's nose. "Is your leg giving you a hard time?"

"She's improving."

Dory jumped. Alec sauntered down the hall from the tack room. "This is Candy. She's on the mend."

"How about you?"

"Healing just fine." His hair was damp and even over the stable musk, there was a faint scent of after shave. His eyes were hazel in the refracted light. Yet another mood, traces of what she'd glimpsed on the porch steps, had descended on him. This time he seemed preoccupied. He jangled a set of keys as she followed him outside.

"Boots gave me quite a tour."

"I knew he would."

"When will you head back to the range?"

"I'm on my way."

"If I followed in another car, could I go along? I'll drive myself home."

His glance was frankly curious, but his eyes were wide, green again and marble-hard. "Today wasn't enough?"

She patted her bottom and watched his glance soften. "Enough in the saddle. I want to see the access road. I was hoping you might show me where you think the rustlers opened the fence. Can we drive that far down, to where you pointed from horseback?"

"We can do anything you've a mind to, Baroness."

Dory considered his glance. "Just in case you're second-guessing me, I want to go out there purely for professional reasons. No melting you into your boots."

"Thanks for making that clear."

Alec started in the direction of the truck with Dory at his heels. "Are you aware," she said a little breathlessly, "that your moods change—" she looked at her watch "—about every three hours?"

"Moods?"

"Tone of voice, Buck."

They came around the pickup truck. "What's wrong with the tone of my voice?"

She looked up at him. Pure enigma. "We parted at the corral a few hours ago with warmer words than these. Has something happened since then?"

"Long day, a lot on my mind."

"Am I intruding? No ten dollar words. Do you want me to come along?"

He stopped. "Yes. It's a damn good idea if it'll teach you a thing or two. You can drive this back. I'm just as well off with only Sundance. As a matter of fact, if somebody's scouting the area, it'll throw them off if they see the truck come and go."

"I might actually be helping with the rustlers."

"You might." She climbed up on the seat and jammed her thumb in the direction of the steering wheel. "Get in and let's get going."

Alec drove out the rutted drive to the main road and turned onto the country blacktop. A country and western ballad played on the radio as Dory watched the endless rise and fall of the landscape.

"Tell me about your business back in Pennsylvania," he said suddenly.

"I own a monogram boutique."

He turned down the radio. "Excuse me?"

"A shop where you can buy things and have them monogrammed. Towels and sheets, all kinds of paper, glassware, just about anything."

"You make a living—putting initials on things?"

Dory laughed. "We sure do. I've been thinking about putting the Rocker L brand on some horse blankets and shipping them out here."

"Monogrammed horse blankets."

"Very big back East. There's a bigger company dying to buy me out."

Alec shrugged. "Lucrative offer?"

"Yes, as a matter of fact. I don't know what I'll do."

"Your heart's not in this monogram work?"

"Doesn't take much heart. Anyway, I could have your own monogram put on your bedspread, or a blanket or sheets."

"You sleeping in my bed?"

"No, I—" Dory stopped, and fought a flush. "Of course not."

Alec kept his eyes on the road. "Feel free, if you want to stretch out. Single beds were never my style."

"I'm fine. I'm back in my old room."

"I guessed as much. I found a hairband and a stack of old movie magazines when I moved in. There's a heart on the closest wall. Dory loves Jimmy, or something."

"Really? Jimmy Delaney was my first crush."

"First of many, I gather. Hope he treated you better than Baldridge. Use any bedroom you like, just keep my initials off the bedclothes. You can carve them in the closet, if you've a mind to."

Dory laughed and leaned back into the seat as they drove another quarter mile in more comfortable silence. Alec turned off onto a narrower paved lane. "This winds its way through the hills and on into Swenson, a few miles farther along. Forsyth's the same direction. This was a Cheyenne trail first, of course. Then it became the boundary between the Circle B out to your left and the homesteaders in the little valley. Everything to the right became Rocker L during the Depression when John Lydon bought the north range."

"From the homesteader?"

"The son of the original settler."

They came to the top of the hill, over another rise from where they'd come on horseback. The fencing ran for miles, along the spine of the land, posted at regular intervals with No Trespassing signs and the symbol of the Rocker L brand. Alec pulled over where the hill flattened out and a gate was padlocked shut. They both got out of the truck.

Dory stood at the low spot with the sunset at her back. "Amazing. I don't see one cow."

"Watch the lay of the land. It slides off over there. Most of the cattle are up beyond the rise." He pointed to a stand of ponderosa. "That's where we rode."

Dory turned and got her bearings. "There's the cabin." She turned to Alec. "Can you unlock the gate?"

He jangled the keys.

Dory's head swam. The view, deepened by the dusk, was breathtaking. The deepening shadows heightened the contrast of the natural rise, which fell away to undulating hills banked in healthy grasses. The stream wound along the hillside and disappeared around a bend between a stand of cottonwoods and the deserted homestead. Without waiting for Alec, she started through the grass to the log house, climbing up and over the remains of a split-rail fence. Wildflowers nodded and a flurry of birds lifted up off the pasture and circled her.

When Alec reached her, she was at the steps. "Even in this light I can see for miles."

"You were meant to."

"Red should have the hands living out here. Nobody'd dare sneak in."

"Long ride back to the ranch."

She nodded, not wanting to sound as naive as she always felt in his presence. He came up beside her and their shoulders rubbed. The burn began, rib deep, as she thought about what Alec didn't know.

Her hair blew across her face and he brushed it aside, searing her cheek and then her temple with his fingertips. When he kept his hand at her ear, she closed her eyes, suddenly aware that he was fighting the same simmering desire she was. No wonder his moods kept changing. He had no more business get-

ting involved with her than she did with him. No
more—

He kissed her, gently as he had on the horse, then
with what was unmistakably rising passion.

"Goodness," she managed.

Alec's free arm went across her back as he put his
hand deep in her hair. "You were meant to love this,
as much as I do," he said as his lips brushed hers.

Twelve

Dory moaned and slid her arms around his back, letting the feel of him weaken her knees. He brushed his mouth over hers and then lightly traced her lips with his tongue.

"Alec," she murmured against his open mouth.

"I'm sorry. You said no man-melting." He straightened up and took a step backward.

"No. Don't apologize. Don't ever apologize." She inhaled. Her halfhearted attempt to ignore the pleasure dancing through her failed the moment he lowered his arms.

Pressure crossed her spine as he opened one hand at the small of her back and the other at the back of her head. She snuggled into him, molding herself more perfectly than she dared to believe, against his mouth, his chest and the flat, warm plane of his hips.

She welcomed him, urged him on with her own gentle exploration until she could feel his desire. Her response deepened as she savored every moment, encouraged by the realization that six feet two inches of raw masculinity found her desirable. Common sense drained out of her, replaced by a welcome heat that teased them both.

As she put her hand at the back of his head, Alec grasped her gently by the shoulders and stepped back. He took one lung-filling breath. "Head clearing time, darlin'."

She smiled. "I didn't think I'd ever feel this way again."

His expression was thoughtful and he looked at the landscape before he answered. "Does a man good to know he can be helpful. Does a woman good to know there's more to her life than what she had all wrapped up in a tight little package. Lydon roots—"

"Alec, please don't start."

"Baroness, I don't intend to stop. Whether I wind up hanging myself or not."

"Second-guessing me?"

"Montana's a far piece for a weekend getaway, even if you did need a change of scenery. You've come all the way out here to do more than get over some greenhorn banker." He tapped her forehead. "It's not me that's making you feel so good. It's what you realize is yours. It's this."

"The change of scenery has done me some good."

"Some good! Yesterday you were a heartbroken, weepy, overdressed bundle of nerves, drowning in a bad case of the miseries."

She chuckled. "You've seen some improvement?"

"Let's just say your potential's beginning to show."

"My potential?"

"For seeing what's going on around you. In that damned understated way of yours, your curiosity's come to the surface."

Her face flamed as blood coursed through her cheeks. She felt his fingers tighten as he lowered his head. This time his kiss was instantly deep, bone-meltingly sensuous. Although she ached for the feel of the rest of him against her, it was Dory who fought to keep the dusky, Montana night air between them.

"Oh, darlin'," he murmured.

She kissed him within an inch of surrender, then put her hands on his wrists. "This isn't doing either of us any good."

"Speak for yourself. Sure gets my blood running."

Her eyes widened. "I hope you don't think I asked to come along for this."

He studied her. "A good portion of the time I don't have a clue to what you think, even when it seems to be written all over your face."

"What does?"

He turned and watched the sky. "Let it pass."

"Alec, what's written all over my face?"

"Any number of things, depending."

She hesitated, then touched his arm. "On what?"

"On the moment." He smiled at her. "It does a cowboy good to see the ranch owner learning a thing or two, even if it's a crash course. Makes a man enjoy looking into those chocolate eyes of yours, deep as the coal under your feet."

"Coal."

"You know right well what you're standing on."

"Then you know."

Alec's playfulness evaporated. "What do I know, Dory?"

She damned herself. "Nothing."

"Something, damn it. There's been talk, rumors on the wind." He narrowed his gaze until it bore into her. "My God, it's written all over your face, when are you going to get around to telling me?"

Dory tried to turn away, only to have Alec tilt her chin. "Or don't I get to hear it from you, being only the hired help?"

"Alec, that's enough."

"Heartland Mining Company wants the seam of coal that runs right through this pass, right under your feet." When she didn't reply, he gripped her shoulders. "Don't they?"

"Yes! They've made us an offer."

His green eyes darkened. "Let me hear it from you."

"For this. The north range."

"You studied that offer yet?"

"Well, I—"

Alec's eyes were bright. "And I accuse you of being naive. Jace was due out here to meet with Heartland. Monday, is that it?" He was nearly shouting.

Dory raised her own voice an octave as she fought her anger. "Yes. I'm seeing them Monday."

"You." His laugh ripped the dusk. "What chance do you have, all soft brown eyes and a face like an open book?"

"What chance?" As she said it, she realized he had no idea the contract had already been signed. "Whatever business transpires is between the Lydons and Heartland. Not you."

"I made your mother an offer on this range, offered to lease it and bring in my own herd. Of course it doesn't come close to the money Heartland'll throw at you, but it might have kept you solvent. She wouldn't consider it."

"We couldn't afford it, I'm sure."

"You aren't sure about anything." He looked as though he'd been slapped. "You know anything about strip-mining?"

"I've studied—"

"Books?" He tugged her by the wrist, forcing her to her knees, then opened her hand on the gravelly earth. "This is thin soil, skin, flesh of the land. Overburden's like the fur on a rabbit. It lays out here, covering hill and ditch, ruts and shallows, giving your cattle nearly everything they need." He pulled up a handful of grass. "All of these blades may dry out— brittle as bone come July, snap under your boot in January—but it's healthy as all get out because coal's an aquifer, an aquifer that carries the moisture."

He opened his palm to the grass. "You mine coal and the stuff looks rock hard, but it's full of moisture, water that runs under your ranges even when there's nothing in your crick but a ribbon of mud."

Dory stood up. "If you've known about Heartland, and you feel so strongly, why'd you wait so long to bring it up? We've had hours to talk about this."

Alec looked up, then brushed his hands on his thighs. "Stupidity. I haven't been thinking straight since I listened to your caterwauling. What a fool I've been, waiting to hear it from you. You've talked about every other bloody thing in your life. Men, monograms, horses...every bloody thing but what brought you out here."

Dory was still pale from his tirade. "Alec, this isn't a decision my family's made lightly. It's what's been recommended and it's not something that's meant to be discussed."

"Certainly not with the foreman."

"No."

"Red knows?"

"Yes."

Pain shot through his expression. As she chose her words, she avoided his stare. "I'm only an emissary for the family, a last-minute, ill-informed one at that."

"You're right on that score. You're just following orders? Maybe when you got on that plane in Philadelphia, that's what you thought you were doing." He cupped the back of her head and tilted her face to his. "The woman who stands eye-to-eye with me, the one who raced me to that stream, the one who rode fences with Boots and asked to be brought out here, knows better."

With concerted effort, he released her, then raised his face to the purple sky, closed his eyes and inhaled. When he turned back to look at her, his mouth was set. "The woman in that crick yesterday bares as much resemblance to the one I just kissed as hardscrabble to winter wheat."

"I've learned a lot. You've taught me . . ."

"Not enough. Have you ever seen a strip-mining operation?"

"I've seen photographs."

"Pictures?" He scoffed. "Nothing from a camera can do justice to a dragline. Six million pounds of crane, big as the sky, strips off the overburden. Pulls that mantle back, and harvests the coal seam. God-awful racket around the clock. Come sundown they turn on the lights so the thing can eat twenty-four hours a day."

"It is a living thing to you, isn't it?"

"It's a bloodthirsty jackal after a rabbit. Dragline strips off the mantle of flesh and digs out the heart and guts."

Dory winced. "But there's reclamation."

"Years from now, when they've sucked it dry, they'll put the soil back. Over what? It's the coal that was the conductor and that'll be gone, torn out. There'll be nothing left to store the moisture. Prickly pear's about all you'll grow. And that sure as hell won't fatten cattle."

"Despite how you feel, and how you think I feel, you've made me fall in love with this place," she whispered, her throat tight.

"Which place."

"All of it, all of the ranch."

"This range is part of that."

"Part we need to sacrifice to keep the rest."

"Hell."

"People smarter than I, the ones we pay to analyze these things, have recommended it. Alec, it isn't some half-baked decision. Loving it's not enough."

"How would you know? How would any of you back there in your comfortable houses, living your fancy lives, have the faintest idea?"

"It's ours!"

"As I am all too painfully aware." Alec turned and walked toward the cabin.

She caught up with him at the remains of a split-rail fence and looked up at him, all shadows. "I'm sorry."

"Forget it."

"No, Alec." She took his arm. "I'm extremely vulnerable right now. After what I've been through with Tyler, my emotions are raw. That's what you see in my face. Being with you, seeing all of this through your eyes has made me feel again. Maybe I'll never know it the way you do, or have the attachment, but it's you who's made me love it. Maybe you shouldn't have. Maybe you shouldn't care as much, either."

He looked back at her and searched her face. "There's not a ranch still working, doesn't have love under it, deep as the coal in the seam. It's a bone-breaking life, not worth a damn, otherwise."

She kept her hand on his arm, feeling the rock-hard tension in him. "I'm sorry."

"So am I. Answer one more question. When you sell this off, how many of us go, too?"

Tears filled her eyes. "You're ready to run your own ranch, Alec. It'll be a promotion."

"Clever way to put it."

"I'm sorry."

"And you all soft and flirting, all the time you've known I was to be pitched along with the range." Suddenly, Alec turned his head.

"I don't know what to say."

"Hush." Fear shot up her spine as he pulled her roughly to his side.

"What?" she whispered.

He pressed his fingers against her lips. The distant bark of a dog was nearly swallowed by the wind. Alec was ramrod straight. "Get on inside the cabin."

Thirteen

Dory was all gooseflesh. "Without you?"

"Do as I say." He urged her from the hug and walked her as far as the rickety porch. "Get on in and stay there."

"Alec, you're frightening me."

He nodded. "I can see that. There's no need. Just something needs checking."

"Thieves?"

"Maybe."

"Boots said the sheriff's department was out here."

"Should be, but there was barking just now. Nobody out to catch a rustler brings a dog that'll spook the herd."

"Alec—"

"Don't argue! Let me do what you pay me for, at least until you fire me. I know this stretch like the cows themselves. You'll be safe inside. There's no time for this. Do as I say." He shoved her in the direction of the deserted log cabin and waited until she'd gone inside.

Dank air and musk assaulted her as Dory entered. She closed the door and stumbled immediately to the patch of illumination at the farthest window. Her last glimpse of Alec was as he came from the truck, rifle under his arm.

Shafts of gray light fought their way through the dirt on the glass panes as Dory turned from the window and tried to get her bearings. What passed for the living room of the cabin was musty and as dark as pitch.

Above her head something scurried across a beam and she backed up to the hearth, finally pressing herself against the cold stone of the chimney breast. Whatever was going on outside—and she imagined howling dogs and rifle shots—was lost to her over the thunder of her heart and the fear pounding in her ears.

"Alec, forgive me," she whispered as she prayed for his safety. Long minutes dragged as she stood fighting the torment of her imagination. Whatever she was sharing the space with scuttled back overhead.

She touched her lips with her fingertips and tried to relive the feel of Alec's touch. Comprehension rimmed her eyes with tears again. The foreman who'd rinsed off in the creek, the man she'd so blithely accused of skinny-dipping and playing hooky, was out there laying his life on the line for another person's ranch. Her ranch.

The cowboy she'd accused of flirting, the cowboy she'd kissed because it made her feel better, was as much a part of this land on which she stood as the cattle above it and the coal beneath it. She cringed at her inadequacy, at her foolishness and stupidity.

The minutes dragged and she huddled with her vivid imagination for half an hour. When she couldn't stand her clammy palms and raw nerves another moment, she took a step forward, intending to reach the door. Instead she knocked over a chair.

With a curse, she dragged it out of her way. Her hand was still at the rising bruise on her thigh when the sound of bootsteps on the porch made her stop. "Thank God," she murmured, expecting Alec to step into the room.

Instead the door flew back on its hinges. Her blood froze as a six-inch wide beam of light caught her. Dory put her arm to her eyes.

"Don't move."

She stayed as she was.

"Raise your arms over your head."

It wasn't until she was summarily yanked around the waist and dragged to the corner that she began to think clearly. With her hands open over the log wall, she turned her head. "Who are you?"

The beam coursed over her. "I had better get that information out of you." A badge was thrust in front of her face as the voice behind her began to recite her rights.

"I'm Doris Lydon."

"You have the right to remain silent."

"I don't need to be silent. I own this ranch." The beam fell over her again.

"That she does," a familiar voice added from the doorway.

"Alec!" She straightened up and brushed herself off as she squinted at the silhouette.

"Ted Durham, Doris Lydon. Ted's a deputy from Swenson," her foreman continued.

Dory blinked. The deputy adjusted the flashlight, offered his hand and an apology.

"You're needed about a quarter of a mile up the access road," Alec added as he stepped into the room. "Stan got lucky."

"Great work," the deputy replied.

"On your department's part," Alec added.

Dory stood still, trying to find her voice as the men talked business. The officer was still apologizing as the three of them left the cabin. As he disappeared into the night, Alec turned to her. "You all right?"

"Yes, of course. I had no idea."

"There's risks in every job."

She leaned into the cowboy. "How much danger were you in?"

"None."

"Alec."

"They're rustlers, not murderers. The authorities have been on this guy's trail. It was just a matter of tracking him to his latest location."

"My north range."

"Your north range."

"I'm sorry."

"For what?"

She stepped away from him and stood alone, hugging herself in the dark. "For everything." The tension crackled and she ached for his touch or a flirtatious remark to soften the atmosphere.

Instead the foreman started down the porch steps. "Night's not over. Time to get on back. I probably ought to rustle up Red and see this thing through."

Dory trotted along beside him. "Do you have to go into Swenson and press charges?"

"Eventually."

"I want to go."

"No need."

"I own what the bastard's been stealing."

He paused. "For the time being."

"No matter how you feel about Heartland, I want to see this through."

"You won't see it through tonight."

"It's high time a Lydon got involved."

"Until about an hour ago, I would have said the same thing."

"Tell me you don't mind."

"It's not my place to mind." He sighed heavily.

"You don't sound too enthusiastic. Got a burr under your saddle?"

Alec studied her, then opened the door to his truck. "Can't seem to get rid of it."

"Can't we call a truce? I love this ranch. We all want to guarantee a future for it. For you, too."

In response Alec started the truck with Sundance still in the trailer. He wheeled it out slowly onto the paved road. "I'll thank you not to include plans for me with your plans for the range."

"Let me go with you to the sheriff's office."

"I can't see that I can stop you."

She settled into the seat. "That's not the invitation I would have hoped for, but under the circumstances—"

"Under the circumstances, Baroness, you're lucky I didn't leave you on the cabin porch and let you walk home."

Although Alec had been right and the business of pressing charges and tracing the stolen cattle operation wasn't concluded in the small hours of the morning, Dory still found the trip into the Swenson sheriff's office fascinating. She listened for over an hour to the tight-lipped conversation between Red O'Brien, Alec McDowell and the deputies assigned to the case. In the bare-boned room normally used for interrogations, the men palmed cups of coffee and discussed theories as they pored over computer printouts that mapped a trail of missing cattle.

Red served as interpreter, making sure she understood what they were discussing and Ted Durham offered a final apology for manhandling her at the cabin. Alec had little to say to her directly, and saw to it that she sat in the back seat of the car Red and Alec had exchanged for the truck and trailer.

Dory finally tumbled into bed at 2:00 a.m. and stayed awake for another thirty minutes reliving the night. The fact that she had kissed Alec McDowell, that he'd laughed and flirted and rekindled long-buried feelings, seemed no more than a crazy fantasy.

At nine the next morning Dory staggered into the bathroom after a fitful sleep and ridiculous dreams. She'd gotten no further than brushing her teeth when a sharp rap sounded at the front door.

She went into the hall as it came again, harder. "Coming," she muttered as she pulled a gold and scarlet knee-length kimono around her. With one hand driving her tangle of hair off her face and the other holding her robe closed, she stumbled to the front door thinking perhaps she'd forgotten a breakfast invitation from Red and Ginny. She opened it and peeked out.

Six feet two inches of quintessential cowboy—cocked hat, open-collared polo shirt, pewter bronco belt buckle, denim supple as old chaps, and boots crossed at the ankle—leaned against her porch rail. She ran a single glance from hat brim to boot toe.

"Mornin', Baroness."

Dory closed the door and leaned against it. Over the unpleasant pounding in her chest, she listened to his bootsteps as he crossed to her threshold. There had been nothing in the final 2:00 a.m. parting to indicate that Alec was anything but exhausted, furious and disgusted with her. Now, as she leaned against the solid door, the screen door was pulled back. The rap of the cowboy's knuckles on the panel sounded right between her shoulder blades.

She opened the door again. "I'm not decent."

He smiled. "What you're doing tomorrow isn't decent. Get out of that oversized scarf and come on out."

Dory opened the door enough to look at him. "Correct me if I'm wrong, but aren't you the one who barely spoke to me last night? Aren't you the one who's furious with the Lydons?"

"I've had all night to think about it."

She pulled the door back another three inches. "You've come to apologize?"

"Hell, no. I figure I've got a good twenty-four hours to change your mind. I intend to give it my best shot."

"Alec, what on earth—"

"Time's a wasting, darlin'. Get into something comfortable. Not that you don't look comfortable in that little slip of nothing. You and I've got some serious range riding and picnicking to do."

"Alec—"

"Call me Buck."

Dory moved her hand from her hair to her mouth. "Don't you have fences to mend or a cow to brand?"

"It's Sunday. Even the Lydons give their employees a day off."

"Go to church."

"God's handiwork's waiting over that last rise of ponderosa." He took another step forward, onto the threshold. "Anything I can do to hurry you along?"

She took a quick step back.

"Don't keep me waiting."

She kept one hand on the kimono flap at her waist and pushed her hair away from her face. "Go back to the bunkhouse."

"Can't. I've got horses to saddle or a truck to fuel. Your choice."

"I'm half asleep, I want to go back to bed." As she desperately tried to clear her head and find words to dissuade him, Alec gently pulled her hand away from her head. Her hair tumbled over one eye as pleasure danced up her arm under the belled sleeves of silk and over the flesh underneath. "Alone," she whispered as he pressed her palm to his lips.

She closed her eyes and felt his free hand brush her knuckles, now in a fist at her waist. Her mind leapt back to the homestead, to the embrace and crush of his mouth on hers. Her body hummed in anticipation of his hands beneath her kimono. She arched slightly as a purr escaped from the back of the throat.

Alec took her other hand, then brought both to her side, pressing them, and his own, at her thighs. As he gathered the silk into each fist, he kissed her mouth hard once, then once again. There was six inches between them. "Change your clothes. A suit of armor might be appropriate." He turned for the door.

By the time she caught her breath, he was already on the porch. "Just one lousy minute, cowboy. You know why I came to Montana. You know what's to be done with this range. If you're so angry, if you disapprove so strongly, why do you keep kissing me?"

"Heaven knows you're the wrong woman, at the wrong time, in the wrong place."

"Then why?"

"'Cause kissing you feels so damn good."

"You've been on the range too long."

He glanced at his watch. "There aren't many women who look as willing as you do at nine-fifteen in the morning."

"I wasn't willing, I was half asleep."

"Or as dreamy-eyed."

"I had awful dreams all night about you and rustlers."

"Or as beautiful."

She laughed finally. "You can stop now."

He shrugged. "There are darn few women I don't have to lean over to kiss. Damn few who can stand and look me right in the eye." He licked his lips. "Mint toothpaste. Nothing like it to get a man's engine purring. What'll it be, Baroness, truck or horse?"

Dory held the robe to her with both hands. "I'm not going anywhere with your engine purring."

His laugh filled the morning. "Don't get me wrong, I aim to spend the day making my points. There's lots to be said and lots for you to hear."

"And lots for me to argue. It's just as well you kissed me now. I doubt you'll feel much like it later."

"Horse or truck?"

"You won't quit, will you?"

"Not till tomorrow."

"Truck. It'll get me home faster once we start to fight."

Fourteen

Dory met the foreman at the barn. She, too, dressed for the rising heat in a lightweight shirt and her familiar khaki slacks. She managed to knot her hair at the crown of her head and for good measure, she again borrowed Ginny's Stetson.

A picnic hamper sat next to Alec on the seat of the pickup truck and she opened it as he started the engine. "Sandwiches, thermoses, half a cake! Did you put this together?"

"Ginny's doing. There were slim pickings at the bunkhouse."

"She knows what you're up to?"

Alec grinned as he kept his eyes on the rutted drive out to the county road. "Baroness, I can't say as I even know what I'm up to. I just know Lydons need some education on the matter of selling off and tearing up their range land."

"And you're just the one to do the educating?"

"I've a proposition for your family."

"I'm listening."

He nodded with his chin. "Wait till we're settled in."

"Where?"

"Thought we'd start where we left off."

"At the cabin?"

"Good a place as any."

Although she tried, Dory was unable to get any more information out of him. Out of frustration, she leaned back into the truck seat and watched the terrain roll by. The June heat shimmered over the mounds and dips in the landscape. She found the familiarity soothing as they rolled along. Dory finally spoke as they approached the plateau of the north range.

"Since it's broad daylight, I'd like another look at the cabin."

"No deputy sheriffs to search you for weapons?"

"No critters to scare the life out of me."

After the usual maneuvering at the gate, Alec drove the truck in along the old access road. They bumped along for half a mile, past the remains of the corral and barn. Wildflowers soaking up the last of the spring moisture, bent in the breeze. A smattering of the cattle were visible in the east, and Dory pointed them out as they got out of the truck.

"Time to be here's when we do the branding."

"I'd have been in the way."

"We'd have put you to work. We had six extra hands this year, including the Haslett twins, a boy and a girl who came out with their dad from the Lazy K. They have a small spread so we lend a hand there, couple times a year, barter our time. Great way to raise a family, all pitching in," he added quietly as he pointed to the herd. "They may come back for the haying. We did all the branding back home, where you and Boots dropped the fence poles."

"He showed me the calving sheds."

"A ways out from there. Calving's another time we call in the neighbors. I spent two days at the Hasletts, soon as we finished. When time came to separate the herd, we had the mamas and their calves far as the eye could see. With Boots and the hired hand riding drag, we drove the studs to pasture with the heifers, then settled the cow-calf operation out here in two days. You want to maintain their weight, but if you can move them twenty, twenty-five miles in the first few days, they're so tired, come sundown they'll stay put instead of roaming into the gullies."

"It must be something to see."

"Some of the big spreads out in Wyoming, Nevada, takes a man six to ten days to drive the herds up into the mountains for summer grazing."

"Have you worked out there?"

"During college. Studied business administration all winter and fancied myself John Wayne all summer. When you work a spread that big, it gives you an idea of what it must have been like a hundred and fifty years ago, driving the herds to Abeline and Dodge City. Ten to twelve miles a day for a hundred days."

"Long time in the saddle."

"Can't you see it, Dory? Cattle, miles of it, plodding over this enormous land. Honest work, dust and heat all day, camp fires and dreams of getting rich at night."

"Alec, you're a hopeless romantic."

He grinned. "Chuck wagons, open sky—"

"Snake bites, thunderstorms. Let's not forget the Cheyenne who were driven off their land out here."

"...Warm bath and a good woman at the end of the trail."

Dory smiled. "Some demure little thing who waited at the window?"

"Demure was never my style."

Something urged her forward. "Some adoring soul who'll smell of violet water and bake you biscuits. Someone who'll ask nothing but 'Have a nice cattle drive, darling?' after she rolls off the bedsprings?"

"You got somebody pegged, Baroness. Were those Tyler Baldridge's expectations?"

Dory blanched. "This is your fantasy."

"There's no bitterness in mine."

She started to walk, kicking the rock-strewn earth with the toe of her sneaker. In two strides, Alec was beside her again. "There's no place for demure on a cattle ranch."

"How refreshing."

"Want to talk about it?"

"About what?"

"You tell me."

What was it about the man that tempted her to open her heart? She shook her head. "You've heard enough of my gut-spilling. This is your fantasy, remember?" She was already entirely too comfortable in his presence, and walking nearly shoulder to shoulder was sending heat into places she was better off ignoring.

"In this life there's no place for any woman except one who wants an equal share," Alec continued.

"In the snake bites and thunderstorms, of course."

"Yup." He laughed at her surprise. "Equal share in the all night sessions at the calving shed, equal share in the August haying and the search for strays, and a hundred other things that make ranching tough as hardscrabble."

"But you've never found her."

"Haven't been looking."

"Not until you have your own spread?"

In response, Alec stopped and watched the clouds kicking up at the crest of the distant hills. Dory stood beside him, fascinated and stirred by everything he'd said. He took off his hat and the simple act made her pulse jump. When he turned to face her, she glanced at him without smiling.

"Such a serious expression," he murmured.

"There are so many sides to you, I'm a little breathless."

"Breathless," he repeated, and touched her cheek. She nodded.

"I have no business—"

She put her fingers against his mouth. "Neither do I."

"Should I drive you back?"

"Probably."

Common sense would have prevailed except that this tough cowboy with a core as soft as taffy had a look on his face that could melt a hand-forged horseshoe. The mere act of watching him gave her so much pleasure she stood where she was. She also grinned.

"What?" he whispered.

"Damned if I know." She laughed and took his arm. "I do know, Buck. You make me feel good. I know you're furious with me. I know you think I'm a rattle-brained neophyte. But when I'm out here with you, when I listen to you talk and you share your dreams, I feel good. I feel alive when I'm with you.''

"I'm sorry for what you've gone through."

"Thank you. Thanks for everything."

His expression softened as his complexion deepened. "Shucks."

"I'm serious. You are the most unpretentious man I've ever met."

Alec put his hat back on and put his hand on her shoulder. "Maybe it's the company I keep. It'd be mighty tough coming up with pretense with the likes of you hanging on every word."

"I'm sorry for what we're putting you through. It's true that without the use of the north range, Jace and Mother feel that we won't have a need for a full-time second in command. But Red also agrees that you're ready for your own place. You should be a manager and we intend to find the ranch that needs you."

Again, he dragged his glance over her. "Are you waiting for thanks?"

She shook her head. "I understand how you must feel. Why don't you just drive me back? I didn't think this was such a good idea."

"In a minute."

As he looked out at the horizon, Dory put her hands on his shoulders in mute apology. He turned around and shook his head, then crushed her against him. "The wrong woman," he murmured with his mouth on hers.

"At the wrong time, in the wrong place," she whispered back as she moved her hands over him. "I know that, Alec."

Slowly, with as much hesitancy as desire, they swayed against each other. Her body already tingled, her bones already ached. She listened to his soft gasp as her breasts pressed to the contours of his chest. Unconsciously she rocked as he kissed her. The languid movement of shifting from the balls of her feet to her heels brought her hips to his. She repeated the motion instinctively as he opened his hand at the small of her back and pressed with his fingers.

"Look at this, darlin'," he whispered as he kissed the hollow of her throat. "There's never been a woman who fit me the way you do."

In response, she kissed his mouth, lightly, then suddenly more deeply, gasping as she savored the physical response of her body. "Physically, you mean."

"Physically will do for now."

Dory wanted to ask about later, but later could wait. Later would have to wait.

"Red O'Brien would have my hide," Alec added.

"No." She stopped long enough to shake her head. "This is between you and me. Do you know how long it's been since I've felt anything but anger and grief? I've spent the last year living my life through Tyler's eyes, trying to be what he wanted, trying to make myself fit his idea of desire, his idea of what a woman should be."

"What a ridiculous thing to do. Best way I know to get your feelings trampled."

She laughed at his honesty. "You're remarkable, you know that?"

Alec made a fist and brought it to his chest. "I've got nothing to go by but what's in here." He pulled her hand over his heart. "Been a long time since any woman made my heart thunder. Darned thing's been pumping double-time since I watched you in the crick.''

''Has it?'' Dory looked into his eyes as he opened his hand on her shoulder.

''You were soaked.''

''I was furious.''

''Heartbroken.'' Her own heart was thundering inches from his fingertips as her breast ached for his touch.

''You're not the type to let a man wield that much power.''

Dory continued to watch his eyes. The green darkened, his lashes swept and, under his glance, she felt his open palm slide finally to her throbbing heart. He slid his hand—palm and fingertip—from one breast to the other and smiled as she took a deep breath. She arched her back, savoring the pleasure. As he teased and massaged, heat seeped up from her collar. She turned her head.

He cupped her chin, forcing her to look at him again. ''Under the circumstances, think we can still enjoy ourselves?''

''I'd like to try.''

Fifteen

"**I**'m not used to... this." Dory put one hand over Alec's.

"To feeling good?"

"Maybe."

"To looking a man in the eye?" He had opened her shirt and found the softness with his thumb. "Second-guessing a woman's the quickest way I know to hang yourself."

"So you've said."

"Don't mix your signals."

Dory smiled, even as she gasped with pleasure. He was waiting for her, waiting for the go-ahead to spin her off in dreams she didn't dare pursue. She kissed him and took his hand from her blouse. "You're temptation itself. There's a selfish part of me that aches to pull you right down on this grass."

"Be as selfish as you like."

She shook her head. "This is enough. It has to be, under the circumstances. This is the cure."

"Can't say as we've cured much of anything yet."

"Alec, to your way of thinking I'm doing despicable things. I'm even responsible for the loss of your position with us. The last thing you need is some ditsy, greenhorn from back East falling in love with you." She kissed him and buttoned her shirt, ignoring his look of surprise. "My head says go ahead, roll around in the grass, let Alec McDowell give you the time of your life, let him give you back your deepest feelings."

"Sounds good to me."

"Trouble is, I know myself too well. You'd wind up with my heart, as well."

"Can't have that. Can't have the cattle baroness pining away over what she's done to some hellbent-for-leather cowboy who chases cows for a living."

"You're a wonderful man, but neither of us needs that."

Something flickered through his expression. The softness stayed in his eyes, but he set his mouth in a smile. If she hadn't known him as well as she did, she'd have thought she'd hurt his feelings. She hugged him. "Thank you. Thank you for everything you make me feel, everything you've told me. You've given me back my confidence."

"You sure you don't want to feel even more confident?"

She laughed and forcibly ignored the desire still dancing through her. "You're an incredible man, Alec. I envy the woman out here who's meant for you." She swept the landscape with her open arm.

"Somebody's destined for a heck of a ride through life."

Alec remained quiet, then turned and started off through the grass. Dory watched. Her throat grew suddenly tight. Never in her twenty-eight years had she had to use more self-control than at that moment.

She followed him resolutely, hoping she'd given him enough time to cool off, as she had. He had ambled back in the direction of the cabin and she caught up with him at the fence. "There was something you wanted to propose to the Lydons, something you mentioned in the truck."

Alec nodded and took a deep breath. "Makes more sense than ever. I want to lease this range."

"You said my mother already turned you down."

"That was then, before it was on the block. Every bit you mean to sell, I want. I know I can't match the outright sale price from Heartland, but I'm offering full market value. I want to lease it with an option to buy and put a few hundred head of my own cattle on it to start."

"Just to keep it from being sold? What does this do to your savings, your plans for your own place? The north range isn't big enough to support a full ranching operation, is it? Surely leasing this would eat up everything you've saved."

"Tell me you'll consider it."

"Well I—"

He took her by both arms then dropped his grasp, as if holding her was too tempting. Dory took a step backward. Unconsciously she began to walk, slowly, deliberately, with Alec next to her. She chose not to tell him how close she'd already come to calling Sycamore Hill and telling Jace not to sell. Now, with this

offer... She shook her head. "I can't make that kind
of decision. I'm supposed to meet with Heartland tomorrow to give them the contract my mother's already signed."

"I'm asking only that you consider it."

Dory looked back at the truck. "Maybe we should
have some lunch."

Alec left her to her thoughts and went back for the
basket. While he was gone, she returned to the cabin
and climbed the rickety steps. She opened the door
she'd hurried through the night before and let the atmosphere assault her. The rambling space was as
musty as she remembered, but the light playing
through the dirty windows broke the spell.

There was charm instead of terror. She looked up at
the massive hand-hewn beams and over to the chimney breast. Some rancher had reared a family here,
maybe generations had passed through until John Lydon had bought it. She imagined children being con-
ceived and born in the adjoining room. She thought
about family, sons and daughters helping mothers and
fathers. Nothing scurried overhead, nothing scared
her but her own feelings. The sound of boots on the
porch made her turn and she waited for Alec to come
through the door.

"Hot in here," he said.

"It's quite a cabin. Much bigger than I thought. At
home—"

"Sycamore Hill."

"Yes. I live in what was originally the carriage barn,
a sort of miniature version of a barn. It has this atmosphere, hand-hewn beams, rough walls. Rustic
charm."

"The feeling someone's come before you and someone will follow."

"I've never thought of it that way. Yes, exactly."

"Is that what you want, life on an estate, manicures, monograms?"

"I didn't search it out. It's the life that was given to me."

"Made possible by the sweat of the cowboys."

"Alec, I know you're angry, but there's no point in going back to insults." She touched his arm. "A moment ago... Alec, do you see yourself in this cabin, somehow? Is leasing this range part of some misbegotten fantasy?"

"There's no fantasy in my life, Baroness. Never been time, never been the money. I've got goals."

"Which you're willing to put aside to keep us from selling off this range."

"Strip-mining would be the beginning of the end."

"I don't agree."

He set his jaw. "I know that."

"Stay on with us after we sell. Let me convince Mother and Jace. Stick to your dream. In a few years you'll have the money to find your own ranch. It can be anywhere—away from here. Once you're on your own place, what will it matter that strip-mining borders the Rocker L? You'll be gone, off on your own. Isn't that what you want?"

Alec glared. "There's two things I want. One's Heartland off your ranch. It'll come to no good, for the Lydons, for anyone who follows. There's tough times to be ridden out, I know that. This isn't some damn fantasy. Maybe we hang on by our fingernails for a few seasons, but we could do it."

"You don't know that."

He looked at her hard, authoritatively, as if his presence might be enough to change her mind. "It's what I know best of all."

Rather than argue, Dory sighed and walked away from him. She crossed the musty room and ran her hand over the windowsill. The sun caught her hair and laid gold light on the crown. "Let's change the subject. What's the other thing you want?"

He came to her, his boots scraping softly on the wide pine floors. "You in my arms. Both are keeping me up nights, making me crazy, likely to drive me to drink."

"Me? I thought we just came to an agreement."

"Out there? You came to an agreement with yourself. I've spent the better part of these two days watching you come in and out of agreements with yourself. I'm telling you plain, because there's no flirting left in me."

"Last night you made it clear what you thought of me and this plan."

"That should be enough to keep me two counties away from you, shouldn't it? That's what I keep telling myself. Then I get to remembering the way you ride, the way you take a horse and make it yours, the way you listen to a tongue-tied fence mender, make him think the ranch hinges on his talent. The hell of it is, Baroness—and it is hell—I was half kidding when I knocked on your door this morning and half crazy with wanting you by the time I left. I was sure you'd turn down the picnic flat."

"Why would I do that?"

"Seemed logical. Next thing I know, you're climbing into the truck alongside me. So much for logic."

"I wasn't supposed to?"

"Don't ask me what you're supposed to do. I gave up trying to figure it out long ago." He closed his eyes with a look of pain from chin to brow.

The desire Dory had managed to quench, ignited again. Tiny flames and sparks singed the remnants of her logic and sharpened each of her senses. The cabin smelled musty, the air hung on her clothing. She heard the caw of a circling hawk and the crazy thumping of her own heart.

Alec stood in front of her, his chest rising and falling heavily under the weight of his confession. His face was flushed. She watched his pulse pound in the hollow of his throat. She stepped from the window, and the sunbeam that had backlighted her fell across his shoulder and chest.

He put his hand in her hair and she trembled. "Dory, I can't stay here like this. Get in the truck. I'm driving you back to the house."

Sixteen

Dory cleared her throat. "At least we need to be out in the fresh air."

"Fresh air won't make a difference."

He reached for her arm as if he were going to guide her by the elbow, but she pivoted so that she wound up in more of a hug. They groaned, then laughed in unison, but Alec stayed as he was. Dory shifted and her breasts brushed his shirt. Slowly he wrapped his arms around her, and just as slowly she raised her chin. The kiss was instantly deep, demanding, meant to arouse what they no longer could deny.

"Are you prepared?" she whispered.

He patted his pocket and then, with warm hands began to caress her from shoulder to ribs. "You meet a man eye-to-eye," he whispered again. "There's never been anyone could do that to me."

"I'm five feet, ten inches tall," she gasped.

"Darlin', it's more than the height, but oh, what a pleasure this is." He unbuttoned her blouse and laid it open, then, with far more fluid movements, peeled off his own clothes. Leaving only enough space between them to move his hands, he unclasped her bra and let it fall. She took both his hands and brought them to her.

The moment his palms warmed her skin, she arched, and her soft cry matched the groan in his throat. This time she didn't—couldn't—fight the rising ecstasy. She worked free from the rest of her clothes where she stood on the rough plank floor.

"You're beautiful," he whispered. "Just the way you were at the crick. All that fabulous height, that wild hair...incredibly warm." Slowly he took her hands and brought them to his own body until her palms were alive with the feel of him. With a devilish grin, he moved her hands over himself, playfully guiding her. Pleasure blatantly transformed him.

He played with her hair until it fell back over her shoulder, then, as if she were made of marble, he reciprocated. With slow, tantalizing strokes, he covered every inch of her. Dory's knees trembled. He held her in one arm and continued with the other until she was transfixed by desire.

Although he was fully aroused, she caressed him rhythmically until her ears rang with her own pulse and the sound of his deep, even breathing. With a cry, he sank with her to the open shirts and pants, their impromptu cushion, and finished the game. Within the space of a heartbeat they melded their separate longings and joined forces, drawing each other closer to perfection. Ecstasy teased them, tore at them as they raced for it, separately, then together in the final drive for release. Dory held Alec to her, as if she could bring him closer still and he moved against her as if that were all he needed.

Against her neck he cried, "Dory."

She tried to concentrate on his pleasure, on giving him what she hoped he wanted, but the stampede deep within her rose to the surface, erasing everything but the waves of ecstasy that rolled from him into her and back.

He lay with her, panting softly, kissing the hollows and curves until there was nothing left but a deep contentment anchoring them to the floor of the hand-built cabin.

"No regrets," she said when she found her voice.

Alec played with her hair. "Never."

She put her hand on his chest and dozed. The peace and solitude was broken only by the faint grumbling in Dory's stomach.

"Another appetite's calling," Alec said as he kissed her throat. They dressed and when they finally went back into the daylight, he pointed to a stand of cottonwoods and pine. "Lunch."

No regrets. Dory followed him into sun and over to the trees. Inside, behind that spot at her breastbone, she still ached. Something tugged at her, something still burned. No regrets? Maybe not, but heretofore, her life was defined by them.

They ate in the privacy of the grove. Dory watched Alec chew. His troubled expression remained. When she'd finished her lunch, she sat back against the tree. "You're awfully quiet."

"I got sidetracked." He smiled wistfully. "Not that I didn't enjoy myself, you understand."

Dory slid closer to him. "Make me understand, Alec. I want to be fair."

He balled his fist into his palm, then opened his fingers. "The first thing you've got to understand is the power you hold. The Rocker L has a reputation for good wages, fair play and excellent cattle. The Lydons settled this valley and made a name for themselves doing it, but you're gone now. All of you've been gone for two generations. Only a greenhorn, east-of-the-Mississippi Lydon would consider what you're about to do."

She smiled at his reference, but took him seriously. "It's all so complicated. This is Jace's territory, not mine."

"Do you want it to be?"

Her heart raced. "I wasn't groomed for this."

"That's not what I asked."

"Alec, I don't know what I want. I've never known." He was watching her with such intensity that her palms grew moist and she turned her head.

He cupped her chin. "Spoiled little baroness, look how much you've learned in forty-eight hours. Look how much you've felt in those two days." Slowly, with only the pressure of his fingertips, he traced the swell of her breasts. "Ranching, farming . . . this is God's work. It comes from the heart and the gut, Dory. It has to."

She shivered. "Do you understand that I—truly—came out here at the last minute?"

"To get over a broken heart."

"Yes!" She shifted so that his hand fell to her thigh. Even there, the heat of his touch permeated her skin, washing her with the heady combination of guilt and desire. "Tyler was a first-class louse."

"We're all entitled to mistakes."

"I don't seem to learn. He wasn't the first. I'm a terrible judge of men, because I'm a terrible judge of what it is I think I want. I came out here hoping I could make some sense of my personal life." She waved at the air. "I thought—even my mother thought—Montana might clear my head. The business had all been decided. I'm only the messenger. The real business will be handled by the attorneys, of course."

"Of course."

"I thought coming to the ranch might give me some perspective. For me, this trip wasn't meant for more than some time away. Time to clear my head," she repeated sardonically.

"Has it?"

"What do you think? I'm out here forty-eight hours and I'm rolling around on a cabin floor with someone who'd just as soon string me up by my heels for what I'm about to do as make love to me." Dory pressed her hands against her face.

Alec moved closer. "Seems to me you're standing in some dusty air. When the stampede's passed, it might clear some."

"You're trying to make me feel better."

"I'm trying to help you get a handle on what it is you need, instead of what it is you think you want." He pushed her hair off of her face. "Talk to me."

"It's not that easy."

"It's been easy till now. It was sure easy to roll around on that cabin floor with me."

"I'm not particularly proud of that."

"Even if it got Tyler Baldridge out of your system?"

"You don't get over one man by flinging yourself at another."

"I didn't mind."

She smiled. Her body warmed. "No, you didn't seem to."

Slowly she began to talk. She told him about her monogram store and her dreams for a business of her own. She rambled, philosophized and admitted to the cowboy what she'd never admit to herself. "It all feels hollow." She twisted a strand of hair between her fingers.

"Why?"

"I don't know why. It's worse now."

"Now."

"Now that I've come out here, now that I see what's really mine. The shop, the way I live my life...it's not what I want. Men like Tyler have blinded me to what I'm doing to myself."

"Don't be so hard on yourself."

"Why shouldn't I be? I've had every advantage a woman could want, more than I deserve, and all I do is foul things up. None of it means anything. I'm numb. More than that, I'm ashamed of my behavior."

"Look at me." He waited until she was watching his face. " 'Rolling around' on that cabin floor got you back in touch with yourself. Trouble with you is, your heart's there for the taking. It's a good one, darlin', and it's complicating your life."

Guilt and confusion darkened her expression.

"Dory, take the pleasure for what it is. Get to know yourself while you do. Forget the likes of Tyler. You've got your heart back. Hold on to it for a while."

Seventeen

Alec pulled her into the crook of his shoulder and the sudden feel of him made her shudder. "I can only guess what you must think of me."

"You might be surprised," he added softly.

"Montana's been like the light at the end of the tunnel. I need to sit out here for another week and straighten everything out."

"Could you?"

"No. I'm leaving tomorrow."

"Then straighten everything out right now. You need to sit out here and realize how important this range is to you and your future."

The range, the coal, the cattle... Dory shook her head. "How did this happen? How on earth did I get my personal life so wrapped up in business?" She avoided his stare.

"In ranching, it's one and the same. Nothing's simpler than understanding that a decision to mine coal changes the face of the map. Maybe forever." Alec rubbed his eyebrows between his forefinger and thumb. "I'm asking for time. You've done a heap of listening this afternoon, hear me out on this, too. Talk to your attorneys, come up with a fair price to lease this range. Give me three years to turn a profit. The Rocker L can support another thousand head."

"You said a few hundred. Which can you afford?"

"I can afford whatever it takes."

"How?"

"We don't need to hash out the how right now. No matter how many, I'll put them on at no expense to you."

"Two herds will take more manpower. The work would draw you away from where you're already needed."

"Leave the logistics up to us out here. It's what Red wants, the hands want. The Lydons can live with it. Time, Dory. Give the Rocker L time. If I can't make it work, then sell it to Heartland."

She leaned against him, overwhelmed by contentment. "You're quite a man, Alec McDowell."

"You're quite a woman."

"I trust you, Buck. It's been a long time since I said that to anyone."

He smiled and turned to watch the cattle.

Dory sat very still and let the breeze play with her hair. She was hot, mentally exhausted and completely invigorated. It seemed to her that leasing the range made perfect sense. He wasn't asking for the moon and there was always the option of changing her mind. She was very good at changing her mind.

She picked up a slice of cake. "Alec?"

"More philosophy?"

She shook her head. "I've made you listen to enough."

"My pleasure."

"Was it?"

He leaned forward and ate from her hand. "One of the most pleasurable afternoons I've spent in some time."

"There's something about you that engenders trust. You've got such a good head on your shoulders. You've changed my focus."

"There you go giving credit to a man, again. Be careful. This was your doing. I just showed you some options. You made choices."

"You listened."

"You've got a lot to say."

"I could talk to you for hours."

Alec licked a trace of icing off her finger. "You have."

She gathered her thoughts as she unconsciously rubbed his shoulder. The warmth in his eyes and the contentment in his voice stirred her. With a pleasant sliver of surprise, she realized she was completely happy.

When she leaned over to him, her hair fell and brushed his cheek. "If you'll drive me back to the house, we'll talk to Red and I'll call home and discuss the change of plans. I want to tell them all that I intend to turn down Heartland's offer for the time being."

Alec smiled. His sigh was deep.

"You sound so relieved," she added.

"I am." He brushed a crumb from the side of her face and kissed her. "You won't regret it." He kissed her again.

Dory laughed. "If you keep doing that, we'll never get back to make the call."

He traced her spine with his finger. "How about giving some thought to handling this on your own?"

"Without consulting Jace and Mother?"

"Are they apt to listen?"

Were they? Her mother and brother had seen little in her but a miserable woman licking emotional wounds and pleading to be spared responsibility. "My mother's dream is for me to take an interest in the ranch. You're right, Alec, I'll go to the meeting tomorrow and see how flexible they can be...ask for a sort of extension. I have more to lose by tussling with my family ahead of time. I'll convince them of the rightness of this when I can see them face-to-face. What do you think?"

He tilted his head and kissed her. "Sound idea."

She kissed him back and when she put her hand on his shoulder, he pulled her gently to the grass. With his mouth on hers, he shifted from casual to urgent caresses, then back to casual until she was spinning with renewed desire.

She arched her back as Alec reached her waist and played with her shirt. She tried to turn her face, to conceal the pleasure deepening her complexion and racing her heart. "You're making it hard to concentrate," she murmured.

He slid his fingers inside her waistband. "Concentrate on this."

She pressed her open hand against the steady pounding under his ribs. "I don't usually behave like this."

He pressed his hand over hers. "Even when you wanted to? You wait for Tyler's approval, you wait for Jace's instructions. Where's it gotten you? The pleasure's here for the taking. Your pleasure, Dory. Same as the decisions. They're here for you to make."

No matter how she tried, one topic continually fed into the other.

"Dark rooms, comfortable beds are fine if that's what you want from life. Out here you've got to grab life by the throat. Make love under the sweet Montana sky when it feels right. Does it?"

"Yes, even though this scares me a little."

"So did camping out here alone in the brush, but there was a reason, there was a need. And, by God, the fear kept my senses sharp."

She gently closed her hand over his wrist and guided him. "We've come too far for coyness. When I'm with you I hardly recognize myself."

"You like what you see?"

"Whoever she is, I like her very much."

"She's a full-blown woman with a mind of her own. I don't run into them much."

"Back there, in the cabin—" She blushed as Alec leaned over and rubbed his thumb along her jaw.

"Regrets?"

"Never," she whispered as he came down to kiss her again. As they kissed, Alec rolled to his knees and straddled her, supporting himself above her. She looked up into his face and laughed. "Yes?"

"Yes!"

Even as she was laughing, she worked his belt buckle and tugged at his shirt. With cattle lowing in the distance, and the dappled shade barely covering them from view, she welcomed Alec and reveled in what, this time, they took the rest of the afternoon to accomplish.

Late Monday night as her plane approached the Philadelphia airport, Dory was still trying to clear her head. Part of the Heartland file sat unopened on her lap as she looked out the window at the glimmering lights and sighed. She'd meant to use the interminable hours of the return from Montana to prepare her case. She needed to explain succinctly why she'd met with the representatives of Heartland Mining Company and convinced them the Lydon family wanted more time to consider their offer.

Instead she was saturated, mesmerized, drunk with thoughts of the cowboy she'd left at the Billings airport. Against her better judgment she'd agreed to let Alec take her to the plane. In the interest of her equilibrium, they'd agreed there would be nothing more than a last-minute drive out, a simple farewell. However that was after she and Alec had met with Red, after she had convinced the ranch manager of the soundness of leasing the range to Alec, and neglected to mention that no other Lydon had approved the change.

It was after she'd met with the Heartland representatives and convinced them to extend the time limit to their offer. It was after she'd developed a glow born of confidence and optimism.

The mistake had been opening the door to the guest cottage when Alec had stopped by an hour early on his way to the barn. The minute she'd heard his boots on the porch, she'd watched from the window.

He'd sauntered to the door all jeans and chaps, like something conjured up from an erotic Hollywood Western. Or maybe he was something she'd conjured up from her own fantasies. Real life didn't produce men who looked like Alec McDowell, certainly not men with the sensitivity and dedication he possessed.

He brushed his hat against his thigh and ruffled his thick thatch of hair as he stepped forward to rap on the door. Behind the filmy curtain, she was already taffy, her pulse throbbing in places known only to the two of them.

He knocked. She had good reason to hesitate. He knocked again. With adrenaline surging, she opened the door and stepped back into the room, away from anyone else's view.

Alec had stood in the door frame and whistled as desire transformed him. He looked like a man too long on the range. "I just came by to tell you to be ready in about forty-five minutes." He didn't seem able to continue.

"I just got out of the shower." She had hesitated, then reached for the sash knot of her kimono.

Alec had kicked the door shut with his boot.

The attendant's voice broke her feverish train of thought with the news that they would be arriving in twenty minutes. Dory listened with her eyes closed, lost in the delicious reverie of the final stolen moments, this time in the cowboy's wide, welcoming bed. Nothing—no one—had left her feeling more confident, more satisfied, more complete. The rest of her life had been a prelude. She'd found substance, meaning, purpose. In four short days, Dory Lydon had fallen irrevocably in love.

As the attendant gave instructions for seat backs and trays, Dory forced herself to look at the file in her lap. She'd get nowhere if she arrived dewy-eyed and lovesick. A twinge of regret that she hadn't called ahead with the news of what she'd done pinched her nerves. She needed stamina and forcefulness for what she knew lay ahead.

Dory glanced at the map, as she had at the guest cottage, and looked over the photocopy of Heartland's offer. She shuffled the rest of the papers and pulled out the range deeds to pass the time. Since the Rocker L was made up of parcels purchased over the years, there was more than one purchase and sale agreement, some in handwritten script. Only one, however, held her interest, the one written in 1932.

She read it twice, then again as her eyes skimmed the legalese and dropped to the signature at the bottom. *Alec McDowell* in hurried script was repeated in typewritten print. *Alec McDowell*.

Eighteen

For about thirty seconds Dory considered the fact that the identical names might be a bizarre coincidence. Then confusion in the form of a knot began its burning in her stomach. If Alec McDowell had been the name of the homesteader, surely her Alec McDowell knew.

Perhaps he didn't know. He had known that John Lydon had bought out the homestead during the Depression. He made no secret of his devotion to the range. Dory's cheeks burned. Why hadn't he shared such key information? What was to be gained by keeping that single piece of information to himself?

The plane banked for its final descent and she blamed her wooziness on the drop in altitude. Seventy years ago, John Lydon had bought out Alec McDowell. According to his grandson, or great-grandson, or whatever the cowboy was to that first rancher, no McDowell had owned his own ranch since. When she thought of how she'd questioned him, how she'd accepted his explanation for his determination to keep the range part of the ranch, the burning intensified.

By the time the plane touched down, one thing was crystal clear. For reasons known only to himself, Alec McDowell had fed Dory Lydon only the information he'd wanted her to have.

By the time the passengers had disembarked, Dory was sure there was a logical explanation. If she could just see his face... A call would have to do, a call to Montana to straighten everything out. With her heart in her throat, she shifted the briefcase from one hand to the other, slung her purse over her shoulder and marched for the luggage area. She dragged her single suitcase from the conveyor belt and turned in time to spot her older brother at the prearranged meeting spot.

At fifty yards it was obvious from his expression that the ranch news had preceded her. Nevertheless she raised her arm in greeting and marched ahead to face the music.

"What in blue blazes have you done?"

"You might try 'Welcome home' first."

"You're going to wish you were back at the ranch, kiddo," Jace added.

"That bad?"

Her brother shook his head. "I'm sure there's a logical explanation for everything. Unfortunately the one I've come up with leaves a lump in the pit of my stomach."

"What are you talking about?" They went through the doors to the curbside car.

Jace opened the back door and put in her luggage. "I'm talking about all of it, every miserable piece of this puzzle. Mother stewed over you all weekend. She worried that you were being too hard on yourself, that she might have put too much pressure on you. She didn't want you to think she was checking up, however, so she waited until she knew you were on your way home." He slammed the door.

Dory opened her own. "Waited for what?"

"Waited to call Red to see how you'd handled yourself. We both wanted to know how you'd made out, whether you'd wanted anyone to go with you to the meeting, whether you'd been nervous."

"Oh."

Jace walked around to his door and looked at her over the roof. "Red spilled the beans, only he didn't realize he was spilling anything because he was under the assumption that your about-face decision with Heartland was with Lydon approval."

Dory cringed and got into the car. Traffic was hectic and it gave her the excuse to keep still and let her brother concentrate. Unfortunately in another twenty minutes they were off the main roads and she had little reason to remain quiet. She turned on the radio.

Jace snapped it off. "It's another half hour from here to Sycamore. That should give you enough time to convince me that what I suspect happened out there is just my overactive imagination."

"Nothing happened."

"Plenty happened—to more than the north range."

"I made a decision that I think works best for the ranch."

"You made a decision that works best for Alec McDowell."

"Leasing for the time being saves the range. He's an excellent manager, as skilled as Red. He's opted to stay on with us and lease grazing land until he can afford to buy his own spread."

"You don't think we've considered that already?"

She folded her arms across her chest and strained against her seat belt. "I don't think you gave his suggestions the attention they deserved. You should have been more serious."

"Serious is all we expected of you." His voice softened and he reached over and touched her arm. "I know you, sis. I know how torn up you've been all winter. I've watched you go from one broken romance to another, always thinking the guy would make you happy."

"This has nothing to do with the men in my life!"

"Dory, who are you kidding? I know Alec McDowell. I've seen the man in action. I know what he's capable of. He's a very persuasive man."

In the dark, she was scarlet, as hot as she'd been under the Montana sun. "He's doing an excellent job."

"Of more than assisting Red O'Brien."

"That's enough." With an angry twist she turned the radio back on and suffered through a series of hard rock numbers she detested.

Jace was quiet until the headlights of the car washed the fieldstone wall that marked their property. He downshifted and pulled into the meandering entrance, then snapped the radio off a final time. Even in the dark, the lush overhanging trees and sweeping manicured lawn were in sharp contrast to what she'd left behind.

He stopped the car at the converted carriage barn and sat with the engine running. "I had instruction to bring you directly up to the main house. Are you up to it?"

"No, but time won't improve anything. Keep driving. I want to get this over."

Jace put the car back into gear and continued along the driveway until he was in front of the imposing stone house. His voice softened again as he turned off the ignition. "Quite a difference out there, isn't it? All that open space and rolling hills and somebody like Alec to give you a tour or two."

"Jace, you can stop hinting."

"I'm not hinting. I'm just putting the pieces together. My beautiful sister, on the rebound from a broken romance, still a little naive, a little too trusting, goes out to the wide open spaces, her heart on her sleeve. Bam! She meets up with one of her most capable employees. He looks like something Hollywood conjured up for a cowboy, he talks like a professional rancher. Maybe he shows her around, explains the ins and outs of the ranch, maybe takes her out for a ride or two. Maybe takes her to see the property she's come to sell. He's unattached, and most importantly, attracted to her. I know what he did. Any idea why?"

"That's enough! Alec was wonderful to me. I won't deny that he's good looking and charming, but he's also smart. He loves what he does, Jace. His heart's in his work and it shows. All right, I was attracted to those traits. Why shouldn't I be?"

"Because over the weekend your social life started to tangle with your family's professional interests. Pretty soon Alec's advice seems solid, worth considering. By Sunday you were obviously looking at our business through his eyes."

"I happen to agree with him completely. So does Red."

"Red's not on our payroll to follow Alec McDowell's advice. Dory, you're vulnerable, ripe, if you want it plain."

"I'm not a tomato."

"Go take a good hard look at yourself. You give every man you meet a run for his money. I should have realized it would take some steely eyed, tight-lipped cowboy to manage a coup like this."

"Manage what?"

Jace got out of the car. "Let's just say it's a darn good thing you were only on the ranch for a long weekend. In the condition you're in, there's no telling how far you'd have taken this infatuation."

Dory went into the house with her brother. Anna Hilliard, the housekeeper, nurse and caretaker, appeared from the back hall. "Your mother's just finishing dinner. She said if you were to arrive, to go on down. I'll bring coffee in just a minute. Welcome home, Dory. Feeling like an honest-to-goodness cowpoke?"

Dory nodded numbly. She was feeling more like an honest-to-goodness doormat. Her confusion and hurt over Alec's secret had been driven deeper by Jace's accusations. She needed time alone to sort things out, time she didn't have. Instead she followed her brother over the polished floors to the dining room. Above the gleaming mahogany table, the antique brass chandelier cast low light, giving the illusion of candles. Maggie Lydon was alone at the head of the table.

She motioned both her children into the room. "Welcome home, Dory."

"It's good to be back." Dory hugged her and pulled up a chair as Jace sat down across from her.

Maggie took a sip from her water glass. "Pleasant trip back?"

"Yes."

Maggie arched an eyebrow. Anna appeared with the coffee service on a tray and left it between the family members. "Shall we get to the matter at hand?"

Dory stirred her coffee. "Don't put me in the position of defending Alec McDowell, or myself, for that matter. All he did was show me how the ranch could survive without losing the range to a mining operation. What we were about to do is very controversial. There's strong sentiment against selling any land for mining and even stronger feelings that once a place as big as the Rocker L gives in, there's no turning back." She took a gulp of coffee. "Out here, where it's all theory, I probably would have agreed with everything our attorneys proposed, everything Heartland had in mind. Once I got out there and had a good look around—" She swallowed again, ignoring her brother's glance. "I had a chance to see things from a different perspective, one I agree with."

"Alec McDowell's," Maggie said.

"Yes. I agree with what he's proposed."

"It never occurred to you to call and discuss this before making such a change?"

"Of course it did. I knew you'd argue against it. I knew you'd think I was a neophyte reacting emotionally. I decided it would be better to explain things here, now."

"We had just reason, strong economic reasons."

"Maybe. Maybe not." She looked from her mother to her brother and back. "What I've done isn't the end of the proposal. If leasing the range doesn't work out, you can always renegotiate. You told me to use my judgment. You want me to be part of the family business. I had no idea I'd become so interested, but the ranch, Montana... Something happened to me out there this weekend. I don't want to lose what I feel for our legacy. I have serious doubts about mining on our land. All I'm asking is that you put the decision off long enough to investigate more thoroughly. Leasing it to Alec gives us time."

"Did Alec bother to tell you that he'd approached me last fall with the same proposal?"

Dory hesitated. "Yes."

"So you knew I'd already turned down the proposal."

"Yes."

"When he realized you knew so little about the business, he saw his opportunity in our weakest link, as it were."

"Really, Mother, you're insulting one of your trusted employees. You don't have any idea how Alec thinks."

"He admitted it to me."

Dory blanched. "What do you mean?"

"I called the ranch. Alec and I have spoken. At length." Maggie shook her head. "I blame myself. I sent you out there at your most vulnerable."

The coffee played on Dory's already frayed nerves. "I've had this lecture from Jace. I don't need another one.'' Dory stood up. ''I'm exhausted. I need a hot bath and a good night's sleep. If what I've done is so terrible, then call Heartland and tell them you've overridden my decision. Call Alec back and tell him the deal's off.''

''That much has already been done. Red's given him a month's severance pay. He'll be gone by tomorrow evening.''

Nineteen

"**W**hat have you done?" Dory cried.

"I've taken charge of my business ventures."

Dory worked to keep her voice even. "Is that all the ranch is to you? You're the one who wanted us to love it. You're the one who's so determined that my generation keep an active interest. That's all I've done. I won't deny that I met someone who made me see things from a different perspective, but it's a necessary perspective."

"One that will do neither them nor us any good if emotional attachment gets in the way of common sense."

Jace got up and stood behind his mother's chair. "Dory's right about one thing. She needs a good night's sleep and so do you, Mom. Nothing's going to be resolved haggling here in the dining room."

Maggie sighed. "I suppose you're right. Take me to the library and drive Dory home. We'll discuss this in the morning."

Jace helped his mother into her wheelchair as Dory stood up. "I'll go back to the carriage house myself."

"But your luggage is in the car."

"I can carry it. It's no heavier than a saddle."

Jace took her at her word and Dory went out to the car. The night air was warm, but sweet and humid, unlike Montana. It felt oppressive as she lugged her suitcase down the driveway under the stars. When she arrived at the carriage house she stopped and looked up. The thick leaves of a copper beech and two towering oaks obliterated most of the sky, but stars peaked through the overhanging branches.

The same stars were blanketing the Rocker L. They dappled the sky above the herds, and the bunkhouse, and the horses in the corral. Somewhere under those stars, Alec was coming to terms with Maggie Lydon's ultimatum. Maybe he was packing; perhaps he was already gone. Dory's old companion grief simmered with the coffee she'd drunk. Tears spilled as she fumbled with the lock and let herself into her empty house.

The charm of the place that she normally found so welcoming, was lost to her as she threw her luggage on her bed. "Damn you, Alec," she muttered as her voice broke. "Damn you."

As she pulled her clothes from the suitcase, she continued to curse the cowboy who had so miserably complicated her life. Tears still blurred her vision, and the harder she worked, the faster her tears ran. They were staining her cheeks and dripping off her chin by the time she threw the new scarf into her dresser drawer.

Before she lost her nerve, she stomped into the living room, picked up the phone and tapped out the number for long distance information. When she'd been given the numbers she needed, she tapped the first one with trembling fingers.

"Rocker L."

"Red?"

"Dory?"

She took an enormous breath. "Yes. I'm home. Isn't this the number for the guest cottage?"

"Yes. I'm over here tending to a broken screen door. You all right? Your mother nearly had my hide. Dory, I had no idea you'd cooked this up all by yourself." The manager paused. "That is, without consulting the rest of your family."

"I'm sorry if my mother chewed you out."

"She had every right to, considering."

"I made a wise decision. I'll stand by it." Dory continued to apologize and to beat around the bush.

"You've called the guest cottage. I reckon you're looking for Alec."

She tightened her grip on the receiver. "Yes. Is he there?"

"Gone, I'm afraid, and in such a hurry, he bent the screen nearly back off its hinges. Flapping like a son of a gun. Wind's picked up. We're due for a storm and the door's been banging and slapping since he left."

"Gone."

"Maggie let him go."

"I know. It's not his fault. What she's done isn't fair. I'm determined to set things right but it might take some time. Do you know where he is?"

"He told me to have his severance pay sent ahead to his mother's address in Forsyth. He'll be back, though, if I know Alec. He's left most everything he owns right here in the cottage. Took his truck." The manager sighed. "I should've kept more of an eye on you. Should have seen what might have been brewing."

"Red, whatever happened between Alec and me is no one else's concern. You're not to worry about it and you're certainly not to feel responsible. Thanks for the information. You might prop a note in the door to tell him I called."

"I'll do that. You take care."

"I intend to."

"Red—"

"Yes?"

"Did Alec ever tell you that the old homestead on the north range was his family's?"

The manager's reply was one long whistle.

"Clears up a thing or two, I guess," she added.

"When did he tell you?"

"He didn't. I read it on the deed."

"Lordy."

"Good night, Red."

"Good night, Dory."

She might as well have been right back caterwauling in the middle of the creek. In fact, caterwauling might have done her some good. Misery hovered over her like Montana stars as she tried to make sense of the last seventy-two hours. There was no making sense of it, not until she could look back into the enigmatic green-eyed gaze and get some answers.

She was up at dawn, five-thirty to be precise, after a night of tossing, turning, cursing, blaming and crying. She pulled on shorts and an oversized designer T-shirt, made a cup of tea, and started to walk. First light was full of the babble of birds hidden in the heavy branches. A flock of sparrows rose as she crossed the cobbled courtyard and headed for the stables.

The main house at the top of the driveway was gray in the dim light, Maggie asleep in the big front bedroom, Anna and her husband George in the housekeeper's apartment off the kitchen. The house would be Jace's someday, she supposed. Jace Lydon would carry on the Sycamore Hill tradition. He and some overbred East Coast wife would have a passel of children and run the Rocker L from the estate, just the way her parents had. They'd continue to take the profit and sink it into perpetuating their life-style, and when profit wasn't in the cards, they'd make radical decisions to suit themselves.

The monochromatic wash of dawn depressed her further. How had it been that until now she'd given so little thought to Montana? How could she have taken it for granted all those years? Why had her parents made that so easy?

Dory crossed a manicured courtyard of holly and yews that framed the cobbled stable yard and continued out to the fenced meadow. She looped her arms over the split rail. Her Thoroughbred was out to pasture, asleep with Jace's and the two they boarded for neighbor's children. Bucolic, she thought as she sipped her tea. It was a life many envied.

She went back up the hill and across the dew-covered lawn. She sat on top of the fieldstone wall that framed the pool. The sun rose, peaking through the tops of the maples until the leaves turned from gray to green. Shadows fell on the gables of the caretaker's cottage on the east side of the property. It had been transformed into Jace's bachelor digs when he'd traded his suite in the main house with the Hilliards so that Maggie could have full-time help.

All of it was home, enviable by any standards. At what cost? Dory finished her tea and ambled down the hill, back to her carriage house. It was Tuesday morning and although she was due back at her shop, she called her partner and feigned illness. There was truth in her fib; she was heartsick. However, this wasn't the same heartsick Dory Lydon who'd let misery overwhelm her in the midst of the Montana stream, not by a long shot.

There was work to be done. A half hour later she was seated back at her mother's dining room table, poking half a grapefruit. "I've been thinking."

"All night from the looks of you," Maggie replied.

"My four days in Montana—the Rocker L—our ranch is the best thing that's ever happened to me."

"Darling, nothing would make me happier than to have you take a real interest in the ranch. But it won't do us, or you, any good if that interest is, once again, tied around some man. This time it was a cowboy!"

"I know how this must look."

"I'm not concerned with how anything looks. I'm concerned with making a profit." Maggie sipped from her coffee. "Dory, even you'll admit that your personal life, the men you've been attracted to...Tyler..."

"None of it has a thing to do with Alec McDowell."

"Alec McDowell. Perhaps we should backtrack a bit and start with him. Now that you're here at home, in the clear light of day, can you possibly explain how it is that you wound up throwing judgment, common sense and I'm-afraid-to-guess-what-else, to the wind? How you came to let some cowboy take such advantage of you? Of us!''

Dory was half inclined to protest. Indignation and hot denial rose in her the way desire had. She wanted to protest that Alec couldn't have used her. Things weren't the way they appeared. But something else surfaced, too, something keener than all the other emotions clouding her judgment: the element of truth.

''I really need to speak with him,'' she said finally.

''Don't we all.''

''You said you had.''

''It was a rather one-sided conversation, although he didn't deny any of my suspicions.''

''What exactly did you say?''

Maggie put her hand on her daughter's arm. ''I wish I could tell you something to cheer you up.''

''What exactly?''

''The obvious. I suggested that he'd used your naïveté to further his self-interests.''

''And?'' Her heart was back in her throat.

''Frankly, he saw you as a soft touch.''

Twenty

"**A** soft touch!" Dory shoved her chair back.

"These things happen. I'm sure Alec was very persuasive. Jace tells me he's quite good looking in an outdoorsy sort of way, although I never thought the rough and ready type appealed to you. Don't go to pieces on me, darling."

"Soft touch," Dory repeated. "Believe me, the last thing I'll do is go to pieces. I've exhibited enough of that kind of behavior for a lifetime."

Her mother looked perplexed. "Fine. We have to get on with business anyway. As soon as the Heartland office opens I'm planning to give them a call. With the time difference, that would be early this afternoon."

"Is it possible for you to separate Alec McDowell from me? I want you to accept the fact that despite how it happened, I agree with him. The range could be leased, although—'' Her throat tightened.

"Although certainly not to him."

"No."

Maggie shook her head. "Perhaps in theory I agree with him, too, but there's no room for sentiment in this transaction. As you know, we're not the only ones in the area to agree with Heartland."

"I can't let you do it."

"Dory, I'm delighted with this interest—"

"It's more than an interest." She stood up. "I need time by myself. I need to think, to sort out the personal mess from what's really important, from what really matters." Impulsively she leaned over and hugged her mother. "What really matters is the Rocker L. Maybe it did take some hotshot cowboy to open my eyes, but you should have hog-tied me and shipped me out to Montana years ago. I wouldn't have wasted all this time on shallow men and stupid shops."

"Goodness."

"I'll be back for lunch. Don't you dare make a move without me!"

Anger and pent-up energy were working against her. She needed strenuous exercise. She pulled on her paddock boots and hard hat and headed for the stables.

Twenty minutes later she'd saddled and mounted her Thoroughbred, Dancer. "Let's have some fun," Dory murmured as she settled into the familiar English saddle and urged the mare back toward the grazing meadow. She was gone for more than an hour, putting herself and the horse through a series of drills that included the jumps in the ring. When she'd finished with those, she headed Dancer toward the open pasture that bordered the property and was used by the local hunt club during the season.

"At'a girl," she called, and dug in her heels and cantered beside the fieldstone wall where she'd watched the sun come up.

With the wind in her face and the horse moving under her, painful memories stirred, memories of a Western saddle and a riveting view. In her mind's eyes she saw the Montana hills, then the broad back and long legs of a jeans-clad cowboy. She conjured up images of his incredible sensuality as he'd led her through the hillocks and down to the homestead. His homestead.

Dory swore and urged Dancer faster. They galloped over familiar terrain as she toyed with telling her mother everything she knew about Alec. Where was he? Who was he? She wondered if Alec gambled with money the way he gambled with emotions. Where had he gone? Where would a recalcitrant, proud, seducer of a cowboy go when he'd been summarily fired for his underhanded actions?

She drew Dancer up at the far boundary of the estate and began a slow walk back. The fields were deserted, the air warm and sweet, as perfect a spot for making love as the hill overlooking the north range. She chided herself for being able to recall how content she'd felt, how compelling the man had been. What had possessed her? What ridiculous mixture of chemistry and timing had made her give herself . . .

"Snakes," she muttered, interrupting the troubling reverie. "Even the ones west of the Mississippi." Fury made her jam her hard hat on her forehead as she thought about her own behavior.

She returned to the stable at a trot, still swearing at herself and the world in general. She dismounted at the cross ties and hooked Dancer up for a long session with the curry comb. When she'd put her hat and the saddle back in the tack room, she began the grooming, pulling the brush over the warm horse hide with long, even strokes. She swore as she pulled. Then she swore again. Misery was back, the hot-tears, burning-throat kind that infuriated her. She wiped her eyes with her sleeve and tackled Dancer's mane with a vengeance.

"So you do know how to groom a horse."

The painfully familiar voice registered along her spine and she spun around. Alec McDowell was standing at the edge of the closest stall. As usual, the green-eyed, wheat-haired cowboy looked drop-dead handsome.

Her emotions fizzed, frothed in her chest like a shaken can of soda, then settled in a lump in the pit of her stomach. "What on earth are you doing here?" she tried as he ambled across to her.

"I'm not one to go down without a fight."

"You'd better start with my mother. Jace's at the office."

"I've been up the hill."

Dory stared at him. He looked a little bleary-eyed and out of sorts, which cheered her. She cursed the lump that reduced her voice to a tremor and the tears that threatened to spill. "How'd you get here?"

"Flew to Philadelphia, then rented a car at the airport. It's up the hill. Quite a spread you've got here."

"This is the Blake side of the family."

"Ranch profits keep this going?"

"Some."

Dory made a pretense of grooming her horse, avoiding Alec's stare and brushing the mare as though her life depended on it. Her equilibrium did. Alec remained silent. "One of us ought to bring up the subject of exactly what happened in Montana," she said to the horse hide.

Alec looked at the courtyard landscaping. "Your mother called it coercion, deception and seduction."

"That's seems an apt description." She pulled the brush down and ached for him to correct her. She ached to be held once more, to have him whisper that it had all been a misunderstanding. She found the words she hated to ask. "Is it true, Alec?" Slowly she turned to face him, silently willing him to deny everything.

He cleared his throat. "I'm not proud of myself. There's more to this than you know, Dory, if that counts for anything."

Her hopes disintegrated. Lead replaced her heart. She managed to murmur, "Very little."

"What I did to you, the way I handled things, was lousy. You'd probably say despicable."

Every word tore her apart. Tears stung and she rubbed them furiously. "It's beneath me to use the vocabulary that suits you. You used me, Alec. You manipulated my emotions. When I think of how I behaved! I did everything but melt at your feet. You couldn't have had an easier target."

He put his hand out. "Dory."

"Don't touch me. It makes me cringe to think of how I must have looked to you. I was the wounded bird, fluttering in the creek, the starry-eyed greenhorn. Could you have had an easier target?" She flushed scarlet as she thought about it.

"I've come a long way to find you."

"I would have preferred a phone call."

"A phone call wouldn't begin to be enough. I need to clear my name, to apologize to your mother."

Dory turned from him. "You've wasted your money."

"And you. You especially, I needed to see. A phone call wouldn't be enough for me to explain to you what's happened."

She glared at him through glazed eyes, not daring to blink. "I've seen you. I've listened. Now you can leave."

"Not yet."

"Alec, get out."

"I've come a long way to talk to you."

"It's too late."

"I'm not going to waste my breath on words you're too angry to hear. You need time to cool off. Maggie tells me that through it all, you still agree with me that the range shouldn't be sold."

"I'm sorry it's your opinion, too. I don't want to see the north range sold, no. The rustlers probably don't, either. I have about as much affinity for them as for you, Alec."

"I suppose I deserved that."

"A little sarcasm isn't half of what you deserve."

The Thoroughbred had been groomed within an inch of her life, nevertheless Dory turned back to the mare and started again with the brush. When she finally stopped for a breath, Alec was nowhere in sight.

She pivoted. The spot by the stall was empty. Nor could she see him on the lawn or the driveway. What did it matter? Her last thread of hope—that he'd deny the accusations, that he'd have some explanation—

had been knotted, tangled in a web of anger and renewed grief. The woman who had sworn off men on
her way to Montana considered the idea of entering a
convent as she put the brush in the tack room. Not
that a convent would take anyone who'd exhibited
such lack of restraint and wanton behavior.

She showered and French-braided her hair as she
got ready for lunch with her mother, then pulled on a
flattering madras shift. Dory still had a campaign to
wage. Regardless of the condition of her emotions, she
was still convinced that the range shouldn't be sold.

She walked around the main house to the poolside
patio where her mother usually ate her lunch before
the oppressive summer heat and humidity forced her
back into the air-conditioned rooms. As Dory arrived, Anna appeared on the empty flagstones with a
tray that she set on the glass-topped table.

"Where's Mother?"

Anna nodded at the gardens. "Gone for a walk."

"A walk?"

"With a little help from that cowboy. He's a
charmer, that one." Anna pointed to the perennial
garden that framed the pool. Maggie Lydon, leaning
on Alec's arm, was apparently deep in conversation in
front of the columbine and foxglove.

Dory's anger pinched at the dull ache that settled in
her chest. "You've met Alec?"

The housekeeper grinned. "Scared the life out of
me, 'cause I didn't hear him. Turns out he'd left his
boots at the door when he saw I'd just mopped the
floor. Appeared in my kitchen telling me he had a nose
that could sniff out buttermilk biscuits at half a mile."

"Buttermilk biscuits."

Anna pointed to the napkin-covered basket. "I was pulling them out of the oven. He's a charmer, all right. Sat right down at the kitchen table in his socks and snapped the beans I'd left in the colander. He told me his mother made the best three bean salad in Rosebush County."

"Rosebud County."

"He gave me her secret."

"Anna."

"I'll serve them at dinner. See what you think."

"I think you'd better steer clear of the 'cowboy.' Had he already talked with Mother?"

"I should say. They were holed up in the library for a good hour. He wanted to know where you might be, then sat down to the beans. Said he'd rather snap beans first and think things through. Charm the birds right out of the trees, that one." Her smile was positively girlish.

Twenty-one

As the housekeeper returned to the house, Dory hesitantly started toward her mother and the cowboy. Alec was helping Maggie open the gate to the raised-bed vegetable patch. By the time she reached them, her heart was back to its thundering and Alec had pulled two heads of lettuce. She watched him catch sight of her as he knocked the dirt from the roots. His expression didn't change. Instead he raised his hand in greeting. "Some fixings for salad. They'll bolt in this heat if they're not eaten."

"A little something to put under the three bean salad?"

His raised his eyebrows. "Your mother's been giving me a tour."

Maggie took Dory's arm as they started back to the patio. "I didn't expect him to know an iris from a petunia."

"Alec's full of surprises."

"And confessions," Maggie murmured under her breath as they reached the table.

They served themselves in silence. Dory's appetite dissipated as her internal battle raged. She nibbled as Alec finished a chicken salad sandwich. Maggie sipped her iced tea. "Dory, I've agreed to hold off on my call to Heartland."

"You wouldn't accept my judgment and now Alec has convinced you, the man you fired?"

"Yes. I've also spoken with Red. He said you called last night."

"I needed to speak with Alec." She looked at the foreman. "Under the circumstances, I'm amazed that you had the nerve to fly out here."

Alec leaned forward. "You didn't leave me a choice. There's too much that hangs in the balance. There was too much left unsaid, too much misunderstood."

"The misunderstanding has been cleared up. All the Lydons know exactly what you did, how you did it and why."

Alec McDowell clenched his jaw and rubbed his eyes. Fatigue was catching up with him. "I've been talking with your mother."

"About more than flowers and vegetables?"

"Considerably more," Maggie added. "As I was saying, I called Red. I'm still not completely convinced, but I've agreed to follow his advice, with which you both agree. For now, we'll hold off on selling. We'll give it a year, possibly two."

"And expand the herd by leasing the range?"

"Yes."

For the first time, Dory met Alec's gaze. She looked at his dark, troubled expression. "Leasing to whom?" she asked.

Alec pressed the bridge of his nose. "You've got lots of options. There's cattle from Wichita and a spread in the Dakotas in the midst of a drought looking to farm out some beef."

"To whom we lease won't be settled now," Maggie said. "Jace still doesn't know about any of this."

Dory turned deliberately to her mother. "But leasing it to Alec is no longer an option."

"I've withdrawn my offer," Alec replied in a tight voice. "Maggie and I have been doing a bit of negotiating. Considering what I've put you through, it seems reasonable that I find another ranch."

"I've agreed to give my recommendation."

"You fired him!"

"Yes. We've discussed all of it, Dory. I don't for a minute condone what he did, but he deserves to be able to continue his livelihood."

"Elsewhere?"

"Yes."

Dory waited for the expected flood of relief. At the least, she anticipated a smug feeling of satisfaction. What she felt instead was loss. "I'm sorry," she managed.

Dory decided to go in to Signatures, her monogram boutique, for a few hours that afternoon. She finished the day with the usual June pressure of orders for weddings, graduations, and a host of other celebrations. There were phone messages, mothers-of-brides, anxious grooms, two floral arrangers and the manager of a local country club vying for her attention. It all seemed frivolous.

She worked until closing and put in another hour in the office. Thoughts of the cowboy were a constant interruption. She wanted him gone, from her sight and from her heart. She wanted thoughts of Montana to be free of everything but grazing cattle and mended fences. She wanted her heart as clear and open as the country she'd left.

"Men," she muttered as she locked up and dragged herself back to Sycamore Hill. She arrived to find that Alec's rental car was no longer parked in the circular drive. She refused to acknowledge the familiar ache of loss as she went into the main house.

"Just in time," Anna called. "Jace's here, and they're just sitting down to dinner on the patio. Go on out. Taste that three bean salad."

Dory went through the open French doors of the dining room. Her mother, her brother and Alec McDowell were seated at the table. Alec and her brother rose as Dory hesitated, then marched resolutely to the empty place.

"Sit down, for heaven's sake."

"Feisty," Jace said.

"Long day, that's all," Dory said to her brother. "Alec, I didn't expect to see you here."

"There's still some unfinished business, Dory," Maggie replied for him. "Alec and George returned the rental car. He'll stay with Jace for the time being and we'll drive him to the airport when he's ready to leave."

When he's ready to leave? "When might that be?"

"That hasn't been decided," Maggie added.

Jace added, "You don't just rent out grazing land without the manpower to oversee it. For the same reasons we hired Alec in the first place, we'll need another foreman. Red will have to put in extra time interviewing, training a new man."

Dory stopped him. "Doesn't it seem a little ludicrous that the man who's to blame for all this, the man you fired for his underhanded maneuvering, is sitting here at our table discussing it, giving you his opinion?"

"I was all set to go," Alec replied.

"This is the unfinished business? Don't you see what he's doing?" She looked squarely at the cowboy. "Admit it, Alec. You walk my mother through flowerbeds, you snap beans with the housekeeper... Let's see, maybe a couple sets of tennis with Jace, or a little horseback after dinner?" She looked at her family. "He's manipulating you exactly the way he manipulated me. He'll sit here until you decide to hire him back and put his cattle on our grazing land. He'll drop hints, work his way into your lives and before you know it, bingo! Alec McDowell is back in the saddle for the Lydons."

"Dory, you're overdoing this," Jace tried.

"Am I? You were furious with me when you met me at the airport. That was only last night, Jace. You couldn't understand how I let myself be taken in. Are you any different?" She looked at Maggie. "Are you?"

"That's not the unfinished business," Alec said.

"Then what is?"

"You."

She put out her hand. "Sorry. No more spell-binding. I can see through all this even if the rest of my family can't."

"I told you at the stables this morning there was more that I had to say. I told you then I'd wait until I knew you were listening."

"There's nothing more you can say, Alec. Nothing."

"I think you'd better listen," Maggie added.

Alec pushed her hand down to her side. "The homestead that makes up what's now the north range was my great-grandfather's, the crofter who immigrated from Scotland."

Dory frowned in confusion. "I know. I read the deed on the plane."

Alec blanched. "Then you knew I'd kept things from you."

"Yes."

He looked distracted, then turned to Jace. "It passed to my grandfather, who raised three daughters and a son on it till the Depression got the better of him. Rather than let the bank take it, he nearly gave it away to your grandfather. John Lydon absorbed it into the Rocker L and kept him on as a sort of tenant rancher. My father found better work in Rosebud County. His sisters all married and moved off."

Dory sat back down. "Why—"

"I've got no quarrel with the Lydons owning it. You did the McDowells a favor. It's yours, fair and square. But the thought of it being strip-mined tears my heart out. All my life I've had a dream of owning my own spread and I got this crazy notion that maybe someday one of the Lydons would sell back the range."

"But it isn't for sale," Dory said.

"Not openly. It was only considered when Heartland approached you. Even if it were, I'm in no position to buy. Not yet. I approached your mother about leasing last year."

"Which I turned down under the advice from our accountants."

"But you never told any of us your connection."

"Why didn't you at least share this with Red?"

"So it would look like I deserved the job or that the Lydons were obligated to hire me? I wanted to do this my own way, on my own time." He sighed. "Both of which I've run out of. The rest of my confession is what you already know. Instead of Jace coming out to the ranch, Dory showed up, your weakest link."

She flushed. "We all know that."

Alec looked at Jace, then Maggie. "We met under unusual circumstances. She was all upset over this Tyler fellow. You might say she was vulnerable."

"You might," Dory muttered.

Alec caught her eye, then glanced out at the gardens. His own face was flushed and he stumbled for words. "There was a spark between us from the start. You'd have been proud of her. She rides like the wind. Took to the ranch like the Lydon she is. She asked all the right questions. Damned appealing to a desperate cowboy about out of options. One thing led to another. I'd been out on the range looking for rustlers. She wanted to see it, so I took her.

"Once we were on the land with that coal seam under my boots, I talked. I told her how much I hate strip-mining, and she listened. I told her about leasing the range, and she listened to that, too." Alec turned slowly and looked at Dory. "What your family's said is true. Once I knew there was something be-

tween us, I used it all—everything I could think of—
to get you to see my way of thinking, because the decision not to sell to Heartland had to come from a Lydon.''

"Me," Dory said.

"You. I thought you might be able to stall your
mother and brother. Another year or two might give
me the time I needed to pull the money together to buy
it myself.''

The hated tears rose in Dory's eyes. "I'd like very
much for you to leave.''

"I will, but not before I finish. What's unfinished
is this.'' He made a fist and pressed it to his chest.
"This past weekend I learned a lot about myself. I realized what I'm capable of, how far I'm willing to go
for something I believe in. I started out not giving a
thought to how you might feel. I had a goal, one I was
willing to pay any price for—in theory.''

"That's all quite obvious now," she managed.

"No, it isn't.''

"Alec, you've said enough.''

"Let me finish. You all need to hear it. I found the
weakest link—Dory Lydon—and off I went, dead set
on one goal. But I never could quite catch my breath.
I never could quite justify what I was doing. Something I didn't understand at first began to chew at my
gut, at my conscience.''

"What there is of one," Dory added.

"I thought it was guilt. Even you accused me of
sinking from one mood into another. I was putting up
defenses, walls you just kept knocking down.''

"Let me guess. You hated yourself in the morning.''

"Oh, Dory, it was deeper than that, so deep I refused to face it until the full force of what I'd done hit me. By then, I'd been found out and thrown out."

"The full force of what you'd done was obvious well before my mother called Red O'Brien."

"I don't mean that I'd gotten you to turn down Heartland's offer. I mean, Baroness, that I'd fallen in love with you."

Twenty-two

"**B**aroness?" Jace asked.

Alec looked at Jace. "I love your sister." He looked at Maggie. "I love your daughter." He looked at Dory. "I love you. You don't deserve any of what I've thrown at you since last Friday afternoon. Whether you believe me or not, I want you to know that I'm not capable of that kind of behavior."

"Treachery and deception are more apt descriptions," Dory said.

"Call it what you like. I'd do anything to erase all of it. I can't, but I can tell you that I love you. You're an extraordinary woman. There's no way you'll ever believe me, I know that. But there it is. I love you."

"Baroness?" Jace said again.

Dory's knuckles had gone white as she gripped the edge of the table. "Was that the unfinished business?"

"Yes."

She took a deep breath. "Well, now it's finished. There's nothing left to say. Jace, you or George take Alec to the airport, or let him walk." She got up from the table and left them there without looking back.

Dory went back to the carriage house unable to clear her head or her heart. As she fixed herself an iced tea, she caught sight of the cowboy striding across the courtyard toward her door. He was alone.

She met him at the door. "Don't expect me to invite you in."

"With you, I never know what to expect." Through the mesh of the screen, Alec looked weary, perhaps remorseful. "If I can't come in, then come out here. Walk with me."

"Into the sunset, so we can live happily ever after? Your public confession was ridiculous. Mother and Jace will see right through it."

Alec pulled back the screen door. "Come out here, Dory. We have some talking to do."

Her heart flip-flopped as she took a step backward. "There's nothing more to be said."

"There's plenty more to be said and I aim for you to hear it, one way or another. Either I'm coming in or you're coming out."

First she damned his green-eyed looks, then she damned his brains and determination. She cursed every appealing trait the man possessed and the horse he rode. When she'd finally included his great-grandfather, she pushed open the door. With a deliberate show of reluctance, Dory went out into the courtyard. Dusk had settled into a syrup-warm evening and she stood on the cobbled drive, looking at him under the starlight. There would be a moon.

"Okay, I'm out. Talk," she said.

"There's one more underhanded thing I'm guilty of. When you went off with Boots to look at the fences, I went into the guest cottage. As I was leaving, I ran into you on the porch and I had the first-aid kit. Remember?"

"Of course. What's the point?"

"The point is that I went in there to rifle through your briefcase. I found the offer from Heartland, the copy of the contract."

She flushed furiously. "You had no right."

"Of course I didn't. I've already admitted to that. Regardless, I found what I suspected after we'd been out to the range, after you'd pumped me for information, played havoc with every hormone in my system, flirted with me and my horse. Let's forget for a minute that I had any connection with the range. You came to Montana knowing damn well I would lose my job when the deal went through, yet you were no more honest in the beginning than I was in the end."

"I—"

"What, Dory? Put it in words."

"I didn't intend to get involved with you."

"Maybe there's the difference. I fully intended to get involved with you. I just never meant to fall in love."

"You're clouding everything! You're turning this inside out. I'm through with words and I'm through with you. Don't you think I can see exactly what you're doing? Alec, not only did you manipulate my emotions and use me, now you have the nerve to lay it all out in front of my family and beg forgiveness.

You're not some guilty kid who got caught being naughty and will be forgiven after some cock-and-bull, heartfelt apology. The fact that you'd have the nerve to call anything you feel 'love' is despicable.''

Suddenly he grabbed her by both arms. "You wouldn't know love if it jumped up and bit you."

She winced.

Alec looked triumphant. "Sound familiar? You said that about Tyler, but it's you it applies to. Maybe that's the problem. It never occurred to you that you'd love anything connected with the ranch. When was the last time you loved anything you did? Was it when you were hellbent for leather on the way to the north range, or was it when you were in your monogram shop putting the names of horses on their blankets?

"Was it love when you dressed and talked and lived the way a man thought you should? Or was it love when you lay under that big sky and welcomed a man who'd met you eye to eye, kiss for kiss?"

Dory's throat was dry and her words choked her. "Love? It was temporary insanity."

Alec pulled her against him and held her until her breasts and hips had filled the curves of his body. He opened one hand at her waist as he brushed back her hair with the other. He pressed his cheek against hers. "Were we insane?" he whispered. "I want to believe it. I don't want to love you."

"You don't love me."

She felt his jaw clench against her face. "I do. God help me. I've waited all my life for you. Since I was old enough to pay my way, I've known exactly what I want, what I need. I didn't think the woman existed who could meet me on my own ground. Saturday, the day you fell in love with the ranch, I kept telling myself to be careful.''

She forced herself from his arms. "Careful? You're nothing short of reckless.''

"Careful led to reckless when I found out what you were really out there for. The clock was ticking, I felt as though that range was quicksand, about to collapse under me. I wanted you, and suddenly I realized that I might be able to use that to save what might disappear forever. It was a package.''

Dory spun away, only to be grabbed again. "Go.''

"Hear me out first. I took what you offered because you were the key to what I needed, but don't stand there and pretend you didn't take, too.''

"I—''

"In that cabin, all this weekend, maybe since you've grown into the person you are, you needed me as much as I needed you. The difference is, you're all clear-headed and off to your lush life. So I got the range to be kept as grazing land. I'll call it even. You're made of the same stuff I am, Dory. You know it and I know it. You'd do whatever it took if you'd been pressed against the wall the way I was.''

"Why couldn't you have just told me everything?''

His laugh was bitter. "Take a good look at yourself, at this estate, at your place in it. What chance do I have? How could I compete against this life of yours, against the men you choose? With that stamped in my brain like a brand, I held on to pride and not much else.''

Dory walked. She headed for the back of the carriage house that overlooked the darkening woods edging the stable pasture. She hadn't gone fifty yards when Alec touched her, lightly opening his hand at the back of her neck. She stopped as desire flooded through her. "We've already played that game."

"Whatever else it was, it was never a game." He embraced her, sensuously moving until they were nearly one. "Convince me I'm capable of everything you've accused me of. Was I ruthless, manipulative, conniving?"

"Yes."

"I set out to be." He put his hands on her cheeks and traced the shell of her ear with his tongue.

"Alec." She groaned and held him as her knees weakened. "I don't want to hear it again."

"I want to make sense of it, and I can't."

"Don't whisper," she pleaded.

He ignored her. "What needs to be said is between us, you and me. I love you. I ache with it. Here." He put her hand over his chest and pressed until his heart pounded under her fingertips. "And here."

Dory let him guide her hand, knowing where he was leading, wanting to follow.

His breath caught. "I thought you'd pull away."

"Isn't this what you want?"

"Want? Making love to you only builds the want. Sunday was a glimpse of heaven. It's as close as I expect to get."

Dory smiled in spite of herself. "For a man who's no good with words, you're leaving me speechless."

"I kept telling myself I had nothing but my own welfare in mind. That range has been the focus of my existence. Except for the ranch, there's been nothing else taking up my energy. Nothing else was worth my time, my plans, or my prayers. Once I knew what was in the wind with Heartland, you were the answer to those prayers."

"Easier to manipulate than Jace? Putty in your hands, unlike Maggie?"

"Yes, in the beginning."

"And now?"

"The way you feel in my hands is like nothing else, no one else, ever." He was panting softly. "How can I deny it? All my life I've known about that homestead. These past three years, I thought I'd do anything." He shifted as their bodies molded, one to the other. "Manipulating and conniving never felt like this. Nothing ever felt like this."

"You're confusing me."

"Don't you see? I took this as far as I could with only myself in mind. I learned what I'm capable of. It isn't deceit and manipulation. It's love, deep as that seam of coal, Dory. I love you. There's nothing right about it except the way you make me feel. Even if everything had gone on as planned, I would have come back and confessed. Just for one damn minute I wish you'd think about what I'm laying on the line to tell you this. Spilling my guts and my heart won't get me you, I know that."

The tears she swore were long used up filled her eyes. "I never dared to think you might love me."

"If I thought it would do any good, I'd spill it all."

She knelt in the grass and pulled him down beside her. "I'll listen."

"I'm not one for words, but you . . . Life with you, a ranch, sons and daughters, it's what a man dreams of, a man who has a past and needs a future, aches for a future, aches for you."

"If I could believe it . . ."

"It's my heart talking. We can run it around six ways to sundown. If I thought I had a prayer, I'd ask you to marry me."

Dory sat for one long, late June, sun-setting, the-man-you-love-is-right-in-front-of-you minute. "If I thought you'd give me time, I'd say yes."

He sat back down. "Dory?"

She smiled. "This isn't the movies. We're not even close to riding out into that sunset. What we need is what we both have plenty of."

"Raging hormones."

She laughed finally, and it felt so good she kissed him. "Time. This is a prelude. If it's real, it'll stand up to anything."

"It stood up to this."

"I want to sell my shop. I've had offers, healthy offers. I want to sink the profits into the Rocker L. That would save the range, regardless of anything else, or at least give us a cushion for some dry years. I belong on the ranch."

"You want honesty and now's the time for it. You're only there in good weather. It's not all June grass and lowing cattle."

"Then don't press me. Let me settle there first. Let me see it through your eyes and mine, a few more seasons."

"I've been fired."

She traced his mouth with her index finger. "Jace and Maggie were already putty in your hands. They're both excellent judges of character. Why do you think neither of them has come down here with a shotgun to run you off?"

Alec looked over his shoulder. "Can you stand one more confession?"

She nodded.

"They haven't because I've already told them what I just told you."

Dory's eyes widened.

"Maggie said it's about time another Lydon put roots down in Rocker L soil. Jace said another Mc-Dowell on the north range wouldn't hurt."

"Did they?"

"Yes."

Dory wiped her eyes. "I want to believe I could have a life with you."

"Starting from now, could you trust me?"

"I always did. That's what hurt."

"Could you again?"

She smiled. "One day at a time?"

"One heartbeat at a time, if that's what it takes."

"My answer is yes, Buck."

He pulled her to him again. "Baroness, you melt a man into his boots."

*   *   *   *   *

COMING NEXT MONTH

SIX SINFULLY SEXY HEROES SAY GOODBYE TO THEIR SINGLE STATUS—FOREVER!

THE CASE OF THE CONFIRMED BACHELOR
Diana Palmer

Nick Reed, ex-FBI agent and private eye extraordinaire, took fright and said some cruel things when Tabitha Harvey told him she wanted to settle down with him. But when Tabby was accused of theft, he had to come to the rescue. . .

MARRIED TO THE ENEMY
Ann Major

Jonathan McBride was special; a man to measure other men by. Stormy knew she should resent her father manipulating her into marriage with McBride, but how could she when it was what she wanted?

ALMOST A BRIDE
Raye Morgan

He'd persuaded his brother to leave her standing at the altar, but that was before he knew her. Would Kendall walk down the aisle to marry Rafe?

COMING NEXT MONTH

NOT *HIS* WEDDING
Suzanne Simms

When a sexy, rather dangerous-looking soldier of
fortune came up to Diana Winsted in Manila's
airport and said she was in danger, she didn't believe
him. But soon she was trusting him with her life...

McCONNELL'S BRIDE
Naomi Horton

Chase McConnell was desperate to keep his
daughter although her medical care was forcing him
almost to the point of bankruptcy. He was desperate
enough to blackmail a stranger into marriage!

BEST MAN FOR THE JOB
Dixie Browning

Someone had to stop two teenagers making a
mistake they might regret for the rest of their lives.
So Rex Ryder and Carrie Lanier chased after their
siblings and remembered *their* teenage love affair...

COMING NEXT MONTH FROM

Silhouette

Sensation

*romance with a special mix of
suspense, glamour and drama*

GOOD MORNING, MISS GREENE Kathy Clark
BETTER THAN BEFORE Judith Duncan
THIS ROUGH MAGIC Heather Graham Pozzessere
RAINBOW FIRE Emilie Richards

Special Edition

*longer, satisfying romances with
mature heroines and lots of emotion*

HEARTBREAK HANK Myrna Temte
AMAZING GRACIE Victoria Pade
SWISS BLISS Bevlyn Marshall
THERE AND NOW Linda Lael Miller
MAN WITHOUT A PAST Laurie Paige
BRIDE ON THE LOOSE Debbie Macomber

SET SAIL FOR THE SOUTH SEAS
with
BESTSELLING AUTHOR
EMILIE RICHARDS

In September Silhouette Sensation begins a very special mini-series by a very special author. *Tales of the Pacific*, by Emilie Richards, will take you to Hawaii, New Zealand and Australia and introduce you to a group of men and women you will never forget.

The *Tales of the Pacific* are four stories of love as lush as the tropics, as deep as the sea and as enduring as the sky above. They are coming your way—only in Silhouette Sensation!

FROM GLOWING EMBERS
September 1992

SMOKE SCREEN
October 1992

RAINBOW FIRE
November 1992

OUT OF THE ASHES
December 1992